What Bit Me?

What Bit Me?

Identifying Hawai'i's Stinging
and Biting Insects and Their Kin

Gordon M. Nishida
JoAnn M. Tenorio

University of Hawaii Press
Honolulu

98 97 96 95 94 93   5 4 3 2 1

Library of Congress Cataloging-in-Publication Data
Nishida, Gordon M., 1943–
   What bit me? : identifying Hawai'i's stinging and biting
insects and their kin / Gordon M. Nishida, JoAnn M. Tenorio.
      p.   cm.
   Includes bibliographical references and index.
   ISBN 0-8248-1492-4
   1. Arthropoda, Poisonous—Hawaii—Identification.
2. Insect pests—Hawaii—Identification.
I. Tenorio, JoAnn M., 1943–   . II. Title.
QL434.45.N57   1993
615.9'42'09969—dc20   92–33673
                                                  CIP

Designed by Paula Newcomb

Contents

Introduction / 1

How Arthropods Harm Us / 2
  Bites and Stings / 2
  Venoms / 2
  Defensive Secretions / 3
  Allergic Reactions / 3
  Disease Transmission / 3

Structure of Arthropods / 3

Life Cycle / 3

Recognition of Insects and Their Kin / 4

Where to Get More Information / 5
  About Poisoning / 5
  About Insects / 5

Insects and Their Kin around You / 9

Arachnida / 9
  Spiders / 9
    Southern Black Widow *Latrodectus mactans* / 9
    Brown Widow *Latrodectus geometricus* / 12
    Western Black Widow *Latrodectus hesperus* / 13
    Brown Violin Spider *Loxosceles rufescens* / 13
    Pale Leaf Spider *Cheiracanthium diversum* / 15
    "Daring Jumping Spider" *Phidippus audax* / 16
    Asian Spinybacked Spider *Gasteracantha mammosa* / 17
    Large Brown Spider *Heteropoda venatoria* / 19
  Mites / 20
    Tropical Fowl Mite *Ornithonyssus bursa* / 20
    Tropical Rat Mite *Ornithonyssus bacoti* / 20
    Northern Fowl Mite *Ornithonyssus sylviarum* / 20
    Straw Itch Mite *Pyemotes boylei* / 20
    Cheyletiellid Mites *Cheyletiella* spp. / 22

Human Itch Mite *Sarcoptes scabiei* / 23

House Dust Mites *Dermatophagoides* spp. / 24

Ticks / 25

Brown Dog Tick *Rhipicephalus sanguineus* / 25

Scorpions / 27

Lesser Brown Scorpion *Isometrus maculatus* / 27

Chilopoda / 29

Centipedes / 29

Large Centipede *Scolopendra subspinipes* / 29

Diplopoda / 31

Millipedes / 31

No common name *Spirobolellus* sp. / 31

Insecta / 33

Cockroaches / 33

American Cockroach *Periplaneta americana* / 33

Australasian Cockroach *Periplaneta australasiae* / 34

Brownbanded Cockroach *Supella longipalpa* / 34

German Cockroach *Blattella germanica* / 36

Burrowing Cockroach *Pycnoscelus indicus* / 38

Madeira Cockroach *Rhyparobia maderae* / 38

Lice / 38

Head Louse *Pediculus humanus capitis* / 38

Body Louse *Pediculus humanus humanus* / 40

Crab Louse *Pthirus pubis* / 41

Thrips / 42

True Bugs / 43

Bed Bug *Cimex lectularius* / 43

Large Kissing Bug *Triatoma rubrofasciata* / 45

Pacific Kissing Bug *Oncocephalus pacificus* / 45

No common name *Clerada apicicornis* / 45

Beetles / 46

No common name *Thelyphassa apicata* / 46

Flies and Mosquitoes / 46

Forest Day Mosquito *Aedes albopictus* / 47

Night-biting Mosquito *Aedes nocturnus* / 48

Yellowfever Mosquito *Aedes aegypti* / 48

Southern House Mosquito *Culex quinquefasciatus* / 49

Bromeliad Mosquito *Wyeomyia mitchelli* / 49

"Cannibal Mosquito" *Toxorhynchites* spp. / 50
Stable Fly *Stomoxys calcitrans* / 50
Horn Fly *Haematobia irritans* / 52
House Fly *Musca domestica* / 52
Dog Dung Fly *Musca sorbens* / 52
Fleas / 53
Cat Flea *Ctenocephalides felis* / 53
"Human Flea" *Pulex irritans* / 56
Oriental Rat Flea *Xenopsylla cheopis* / 56
Bees / 56
Honey Bee *Apis mellifera* / 56
Sonoran Carpenter Bee *Xylocopa sonorina* / 59
Wasps / 59
Western Yellowjacket *Paravespula pensylvanica* / 59
"Common Yellowjacket" *Paravespula vulgaris* / 60
Common Paper Wasp *Polistes exclamans* / 60
Muddauber *Sceliphron caementarium* / 60
Other Bees and Wasps / 60
Ants / 62
Fire Ant *Solenopsis geminata* / 62
Argentine Ant *Iridomyrmex humilis* / 63
No common name *Iridomyrmex glaber* / 64
Mexican Ant *Pseudomyrmex gracilis mexicanus* / 64
Pharoah Ant *Monomorium pharaonis* / 64

References / 65
Acknowledgments / 67
Index / 69

Introduction

Most insects and their relatives go quietly about their business and never disturb us. A few of them have life-styles that occasionally place them in conflict with us. Some inject poisons, some spread diseases, some bite, and some sting. It is important to note that the arthropods that sometimes threaten us were not specifically designed to hurt us. The toxic chemicals often produced by these animals protect them from their enemies or help them do their jobs in nature, and many of these animals do their part in keeping populations of other insects and their relatives at reasonable levels. Numbers of deaths from insect, spider, and scorpion bites or stings are quite low when compared to those from other causes. Much of the fear about insects and spiders and their kin may be the fear of the unknown. We hope this book will help acquaint teachers and physicians, as well as the general reader, with some of these helpful animals that may, at times, affect us adversely.

The insects, spiders, mites, ticks, and other animals included in this book are collectively referred to as arthropods. They are members of the phylum Arthropoda, or animals with jointed legs.

Though most of the poisonous arthropods in Hawai'i are easily identifiable, some, especially the spiders and mites, may not be. Sometimes it is useful for a physician to know which animal was responsible for a wound to aid in diagnosis and proper treatment. So if you have any doubt as to the identity of the creature that bit or stung you, capture it if you can safely do so. In cases where the animals are very small—as mites and lice are—you may wish to stick them onto transparent tape (see Fig. 17) for transport to the identifying agency; but try not to crush the specimens, because it makes them much more difficult to identify.

This book is organized beginning with the non-insect groups (spiders, mites, ticks, scorpions, centipedes, and millipedes), followed by the insects. A group name (Spiders, Flies, etc.) begins a section. A common name (e.g., Black Widow) begins each entry; the scientific name, in *italics,* is placed on the same line and to the right of the common name. If a Hawaiian name is available for a group or for a specific entry, it is placed in *italics* beneath the group or common name. The common names are those given in *Common Names of Insects and Related Organisms* by the Hawaiian Entomological Society. Those not listed by the Society in that publication are placed in quotation marks.

Under each species, the usual symptoms of bites, stings, or other effects on humans are described briefly. Infants, young children, and the elderly are usually at higher risk; because of their smaller body size or less robust health, the effects of venoms may be more pronounced and thus more dangerous. For bee and wasp stings, the highest risk seems to be in those over 40 years of age. Symptoms and reactions vary among individuals; we have reported a range of known effects, but you may exhibit only a few of them. You may also be particularly sensitive or allergic to poisons or secretions of certain arthropods. For all these reasons, see a doctor immediately if the reaction is unexpected or severe.

Included in this book are some arthropods that are not harmful to humans but may be mistakenly assumed to bite or sting (for example, the *Toxorhynchites* mosquitoes, introduced into Hawai'i to control biting mosquitoes). Also included are cockroaches, house dust mites, and some of the flies that may indirectly affect the health of humans by spreading diseases or causing allergic reactions.

We have tried to cover as many species as possible, but this book is not intended to be all-inclusive. Many arthropods produce secretions that may affect humans, and many reactions are unrecorded. Other arthropods (e.g., beetles, katydids, dragonfly nymphs) can also bite, but their bites are usually accidental and not often consequential.

When an animal bites or stings you, several injuries may occur. First is the mechanical injury from the bite or insertion of the stinger. Second is the possible reaction to the injection of venom or other irritating fluid. Third is the possible introduction of disease-causing microorganisms.

How Arthropods Harm Us

Bites and Stings

The difference between a bite and a sting is simple. Bites are delivered by mouthparts, stings are delivered by structures at the end of the abdomen, usually modified egg-laying devices. In the insects, only the Hymenoptera (bees, wasps, and ants) can sting. The only other stinging arthropod in Hawai'i is the scorpion. The rest of the insects and their kin bite. Bites may occur by pinching or piercing. Pinching bites occur when the mandibles ("jaws") are closed horizontally, pinching and occasionally penetrating the skin. This type of bite is seen in ants and wasps (some ants and wasps both sting and bite), beetles, and cockroaches (yes, they *can* bite). Piercing bites usually occur when the mouthparts have been modified into a tube that penetrates the skin. Examples of such biters are mosquitoes, true bugs, and ticks. Spiders and centipedes use their fangs in a pinching motion, but also pierce the skin.

Venoms

Arthropods produce many different chemicals for activities ranging from communication to defense. Venoms are quick-acting chemicals that are injected into victims by mouthparts or stingers. Venoms are usually used to overcome prey, but are also used for defense. The effects of venoms on humans vary depending on the age, body weight, and health of the person bitten, and on the sensitivity of the individual to the chemicals in the venom. Saliva also qualifies as a venom, as it is often injected along with the bite, and humans may react to the saliva. Spiders, bees and wasps, centipedes, and scorpions produce venoms; reactions to saliva are often seen in bug and mosquito bites.

Defensive Secretions

Other arthropods may not sting or bite, but instead produce a defensive chemical to protect themselves. These chemicals may be a gas or fluid ejected forcefully or oozed out and may be irritating or caustic on contact with the skin. Examples of animals using defensive secretions are the millipedes and several beetles.

Allergic Reactions

Some people are allergic to bee or wasp stings. These people are hypersensitive to the chemicals in the venom because of previous exposure or individual sensitivity. Hypersensitive individuals can take certain measures to reduce their risk. One is avoidance, or just staying away from sites frequented by bees and wasps. This may not be so easy and might mean a major modification in behavior. Another is to carry a sting kit that can stop the onset of a severe reaction. Still another is to undergo immunotherapy treatments to reduce sensitivity to the venoms.

Contact with hairs, scales, or even parts of some arthropods causes allergic reactions in some people. The reactions may range from asthma to hives and may occur just from breathing in dust containing these arthropod parts.

Disease Transmission

Though some insects discussed in this book are potential carriers of disease organisms, this does not mean that the disease is always transmitted. Disease transmission requires the presence of the carrier (arthropod vector) and the disease organism simultaneously. In Hawai'i, the carrier insects may be present, but the diseases associated with them do not occur or are uncommon; conversely, the disease may be known in Hawai'i, but the carrier insect may not be present. For example, although humans with malaria visit or return to Hawai'i after exposure elsewhere, the *Anopheles* mosquito that picks up the *Plasmodium* (malaria organism) and transfers it to another human while feeding does not occur in Hawai'i.

Structure of Arthropods

All arthropods are joint-legged; that is, they have legs segmented into parts that are hinged together. Arthropods also have exoskeletons, or hardened coverings, that surround the body fluids and internal parts and provide support for the attachment of muscles and organs. Arthropod bodies are segmented and contain an open circulatory system, one without a system of veins and arteries. A simple brain and often a nerve bundle (ganglion) associated with each body segment usually make up the nervous system. Simple diagrams of body types of the major arthropods are shown in the diagram on page 4.

Life Cycle

Arthropods usually begin as eggs (though some are born alive) and hatch into an immature stage. As a result of their exoskeleton design, arthropods must molt, or shed their skin, to grow. Several molts, or immature stages, may occur before the arthropod reaches adulthood. In insects, two different patterns occur in growth and development. In hemimetabolous insects, the young look like the adults, but don't have wings. These young, called nymphs, often compete with the adults for the same type of food. Insects in this category include cockroaches and true bugs. In holometabolous insects, the young do not look like the adult and usually are in a niche (the role of an organism in its habitat) quite different from that of the adult. The young, called larvae, enter one last stage, the pupa, before becoming adults. Insects in this category are beetles, flies, bees, and wasps.

Recognition of Insects and Their Kin

Five classes of arthropods are living today: insects, arachnids (spiders, mites, ticks, and scorpions), millipedes, centipedes, and crustaceans (including sowbugs, crayfish, lobsters, and crabs). Other arthropods, such as the trilobites, are long extinct. Among these classes, the insects are the most numerous, with nearly a million species described. With such an enormous range of organisms, the first task in recognizing individual species is to group them by their similarities and differences. Classification of these animals, or in biological terms, their taxonomy, is thus based on arranging these animals into closely related groups.

The most important category, and the key to recognition and classification, is

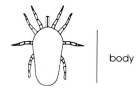

TICKS & MITES
Four pairs legs
No antennae
Body saclike

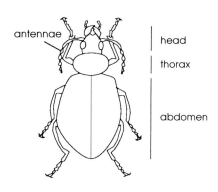

cephalothorax

abdomen

SPIDERS
Four pairs legs
No antennae
Body in two distinct regions

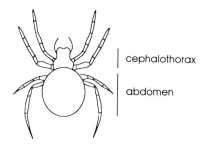

antennae

head

thorax

abdomen

INSECTS
Three pairs of legs
One pair of antennae
Body in three distinct regions

DIAGRAM. Body structures of three major groups of arthropods: ticks and mites, spiders, and insects.

the species. A species includes all individuals that have common morphological, physiological, and behavioral characteristics and can be crossed to produce fertile offspring. A species always is identified by two Latin names, the first of which gives the genus to which the species belongs. For example, *Latrodectus mactans,* the Southern Black Widow spider, belongs to the genus *Latrodectus.* Notice that the genus is always capitalized and the species name is always lower case. Other species closely related to the Black Widow also belong to this genus (for example, *Latrodectus geometricus,* the Brown Widow). Related species are grouped in genera, related genera in families, related families in orders, and so on. For example, the full classification for the Southern Black Widow spider is as follows:

> Kingdom Animalia
> Phylum Arthropoda
> Class Arachnida
> Subclass Araneae
> Family Theridiidae
> Genus *Latrodectus*
> Species *mactans*

The chart on the following pages shows some of the higher categories for the arthropods included in this book and the most important features used to group them together.

Where to Get More Information

The following organizations or agencies will be able to help you with questions about arthropods and their identification. For medical questions, you should consult a physician.

About Poisoning

Poison Center, Oʻahu, 1319 Punahou St., Honolulu, HI 96826, Ph. 941-4411. This is the only poison center in the Pacific Basin.

About Insects

Bishop Museum, Department of Entomology, P.O. Box 19000-A, Honolulu, HI 96817, Ph. 848-4194.

Hawaii State Department of Agriculture, Plant Industry Division, 1428 S. King St., Honolulu, HI 96814, Ph. 973-9530.

Hawaii State Department of Health, Vector Control Branch (Oʻahu), 2611 Kilihau St., Honolulu, HI 96819, Ph. 831-6767.

Vector Control branches on other islands:
Hilo, Hawaiʻi, Ph. 933-4386;
Kona, Hawaiʻi, Ph. 322-0033;
Maui, Ph. 877-2451;
Molokaʻi, Ph. 567-6161;
and Kauaʻi, Ph. 241-3306.

University of Hawaii at Manoa, Agricultural Diagnostic Service Center, 1910 East-West Road, Sherman 134, Honolulu, HI 96822, Ph. 956-6706.

On the island of Hawaiʻi:
875 Komohana St.,
Hilo, HI 96720,
Ph. 959-9155.

INSECTS AND THEIR KIN

Phylum Arthropoda
- Body segmented
- External skeleton
- Paired, jointed appendages

Spiders, Mites, Ticks, Scorpions
Class Arachnida
- Eight legs in four pairs
- One or two body regions; the front is called the cephalothorax (head plus chest) and the back is the abdomen
- No antennae

Spiders
Subclass Araneae
- Body constricted where it joins the cephalothorax
- Body not segmented

Mites and Ticks
Subclass Acari
- Body round or oval, baglike, not segmented

Scorpions
Subclass Scorpione
- Front appendages large and clawlike
- End of abdomen usually curved upward, ending in a sting

Centipedes

Class Chilopoda

- Many legs, one pair on each segment
- Long, flat body with many segments
- One pair of antennae

Millipedes

Class Diplopoda

- Many legs, two pairs on each segment
- Wormlike, cylindrical body
- One pair of antennae

Insects

Class Insecta

- Six legs in three pairs
- Three body regions: head, thorax, abdomen
- Usually one or two pair of wings
- One pair of antennae

Cockroaches

Order Blattaria

- Hindlegs similar to middle legs, adapted for walking
- Antennae long, slender
- Chewing mouthparts
- Young resemble adults

Lice

Order Anoplura (Sucking Lice)

- Flattened top to bottom
- Sucking mouthparts
- Young resemble adults

Thrips

Order Thysanoptera

- Small, very narrow body
- If winged, 2 pairs wings fringed with long hairs
- Piercing/sucking mouthparts
- Young resemble adults

True Bugs

Order Hemiptera

- Usually two pairs of wings
- Piercing/sucking mouthparts
- Young resemble adults

Beetles

Order Coleoptera

- Two pairs wings, first pair thick and leathery
- Wings usually meet in a straight line down back
- Chewing mouthparts
- Young (grubs) do not resemble adults

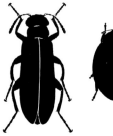

Flies and Mosquitoes

Order Diptera

- Usually one pair of wings
- Second pair of wings formed into slender, knobbed structures (halteres)
- Sucking/lapping/piercing mouthparts
- Young (maggots, larvae, wigglers) do not resemble adults

Fleas

Order Siphonaptera

- Small, wingless
- Body greatly flattened side to side
- Usually many spines on the body
- Legs expanded for jumping

Bees, Wasps, Ants

Order Hymenoptera

- Two pairs of wings or wingless
- Forewings larger than hindwings and usually hooked together
- Young do not resemble adults

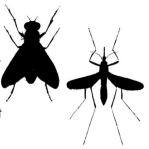

Insects and Their Kin around You

ARACHNIDA

SPIDERS
Subclass Araneae
lanalana, lalana, nananana

Spiders are eight-legged predators equipped with fangs used to inject poison into their prey. Spiders are very useful in helping control populations of insects and other arthropods. Most spiders are not usually aggressive and bites to humans occur when the spiders are attempting to protect themselves. The only truly dangerous species in Hawai'i are the widow spiders, but several other species are able to inflict painful bites and slow-to-heal wounds. Although numerous spiders are native to Hawai'i, all the ones listed here are introduced.

Southern Black Widow
Latrodectus mactans (Figs. 1–5)

A dark, globular, distinctively marked spider noted for its potent venom that is dangerous to humans.

How to Recognize:

The glossy black to dull brown female usually has a bright red, hourglass-shaped mark on her underside. The smaller male often has yellow markings at the sides of his abdomen. Females are ⅜ inch long, males ⅛ inch. The cream-colored egg sacs are rounded, smooth, and papery looking. The appearance of the egg case will help distinguish the Southern Black Widow from the Brown Widow (see Brown Widow). Young spiderlings often have colorful patterns on the tops of their bodies. Some spider specialists call the Hawai'i version of the Black Widow *Latrodectus hesperus,*

FIGURE I. Adult female Southern Black Widow with its smooth egg case. (Photo by G. Nishida)

9

FIGURE 2. A well-fed, adult female Southern Black Widow showing its smooth egg case and typically messy web. (VWR)

FIGURE 3. The underside of the abdomen of the Southern Black Widow reveals its characteristic red hourglass marking. (VWR)

but we follow published accounts in which *L. mactans* and *L. hesperus* are treated as separate species in Hawai'i.

Where Found:

These spiders were first collected in Hawai'i in 1925. They are found in the drier regions of all inhabited islands. Southern Black Widows are usually in dark, out-of-the way places such as basements, garages, storage sheds, or tunnels, and like to place their webs around crevices, wood piles, or stacks of any kind. Southern Black Widows are not as common in Hawai'i as Brown Widows.

What It Does:

The female spins a coarse, messy web in a dark, sheltered place usually near ground level and feeds on insects caught in the web. A web may contain one to several egg sacs. Widow spiders are active mostly at night. Females have been described as shy and usually bite only in self-defense; males apparently do not bite, or cannot penetrate the skin.

If You Are Bitten:

Two tiny red spots usually mark the entry of the widow's fangs. The bite usually feels like a pinprick. The venom is very toxic, and the reaction to the bite

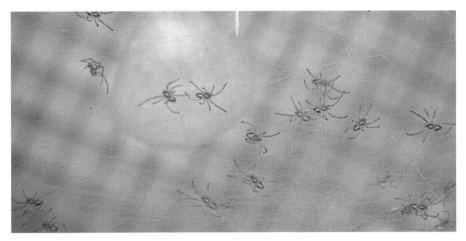

FIGURE 4. Newly hatched Southern Black Widow spiderlings surrounding the egg case. (VWR)

FIGURE 5. Young Southern Black Widows showing the colorful patterns on the tops of their abdomens. (VWR)

depends on the amount injected. Bites of the Black Widow are noted most for effects to the central nervous system, but skin reactions can occur. An intense burning sensation and excruciating pain around the bite site may be felt, and heavy sweating or salivation and nausea and vomiting may follow. Severe cramps, rigid abdominal muscles, convulsions, and shock may also occur.

Symptoms may appear immediately after the bite, or up to several hours afterwards. In severe cases, the poison may also cause breathing problems, slurred speech, and paralysis. First aid other than antiseptic on the bite should not be given. If you are bitten, stay calm and **seek medical treatment at once**. Children and elderly persons with medical problems are at highest risk. Less than 1% of those bitten by Black Widows die, most of those from untreated bites. A specific antivenin is available and should be given as soon as possible.

Brown Widow

Latrodectus geometricus (Fig. 6)

Similar to and often mistaken for the Southern Black Widow, the Brown Widow is also venomous but somewhat less dangerous than its infamous relative.

How to Recognize:

This spider is usually mottled brown or gray with blackish, red, and yellow markings, occasionally entirely black. The mark on the underside is dull orange or reddish and varies from an hourglass shape to two dots. The spider

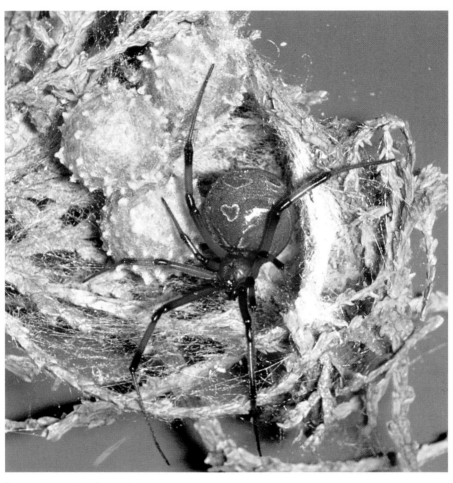

FIGURE 6. An adult female Brown Widow with three egg cases. Coloration on the female spider is variable, ranging from a multicolor, as seen here, to black. Note the bumpy outline of the egg sac, which helps distinguish the Brown from the Black Widow. (photo by L. M. Nakahara)

is similar in size to the Black Widow. Scattered tufts of silk give the Brown Widow egg sacs a bumpy outline (the Southern Black Widow's egg sac appears smooth). Most of the widow spiders brought to the Bishop Museum for identification are Brown Widows.

Where Found:

The Brown Widow spider was first noticed in Hawai'i in 1939, but probably arrived several years earlier. Found on all major islands in Hawai'i, the Brown Widow is generally more widespread than the Southern Black Widow, but it also prefers dark, out-of-the way locations and spins its web near ground level.

What It Does:

Its habits are similar to those of the Southern Black Widow, but the Brown Widow seems less likely to bite, or it injects less venom than the Southern Black Widow.

If You Are Bitten:

Brown Widow venom is potent, but only about $\frac{1}{4}$ to $\frac{1}{10}$ as strong as that of the Southern Black Widow. However, if you are bitten, treat your condition as serious and **get medical help quickly**.

Western Black Widow

Latrodectus hesperus

The Western Black Widow was first collected on Moloka'i in 1943 and has since spread to O'ahu, Maui, and Midway. *Latrodectus hesperus* is similar in size, shape, and markings to the Southern Black Widow and the Brown Widow. Bites from the Western Black Widow should be treated like those of the Southern Black Widow.

Brown Violin Spider

Loxosceles rufescens (Figs. 7–8)

A long-legged, yellowish spider whose bite may cause severe pain and a slow-to-heal gangrenous wound.

How to Recognize:

The Brown Violin Spider's carapace (top of the body behind the head area) is light yellowish brown tinged with reddish orange and carries a faint, violin-shaped mark (with the violin's neck pointing backward). Violin spiders have six eyes arranged in pairs in a semicircle surrounding the base of the violin; most spiders have eight eyes. The abdomen is pale brownish gray. The legs are fairly long. The females are about $\frac{5}{16}$ inch long, the males about $\frac{1}{4}$ inch long.

Where Found:

Loxosceles rufescens is widely distributed over the world. It arrived in Hawai'i probably from Australia about 1977. It is reported from O'ahu, Kaua'i, and Maui and has been found under old boards and loosened bark.

What It Does:

The Brown Violin Spider is a close relative of the infamous Brown Recluse of the southern and central United States, which does not occur in Hawai'i. Their habits are similar, although the venom of the species in Hawai'i seems to be less toxic. Violin spiders live in dark places and spin large, irregular, sheetlike, bluish webs. They are active at night and are not aggressive. Both males and females are venomous. The first confirmed bite (in 1977) was in Lanikai on O'ahu, where a woman was bitten on the heel. Other bites have been on fingers when the victims were moving firewood or cardboard refuse.

If You Are Bitten:

The venom of this spider contains a cell-destroying factor that may cause skin

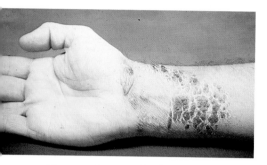

FIGURE 7. An example of the lesions caused by the venom of *Loxosceles* spiders. The lesions shown are from the bite of a Brown Recluse, which does not occur in Hawai'i. (VWR)

and surrounding tissue to die. Bites are usually on arms and legs and reactions may range from mild redness to serious tissue destruction. A slight stinging sensation is sometimes followed by intense pain. Often the victim is not aware of a bite until several hours later. Blistering, swelling, or reddening may occur around the bitten area. In a day or so, the skin may turn purple, followed in a week or so by blackening as the cells die. Tissue eventually sloughs away, sometimes leaving large pits in the skin. Healing may take several weeks. If not properly treated, gangrene may result. If bitten, clean the wound and apply antiseptic. Surface treatment of the bite may not stop additional damage to the skin, so it is important to **see a doctor as**

FIGURE 8. Brown Violin Spider, with the backward-pointing violin visible on the carapace. This spider is closely related to the notorious Brown Recluse, which also has a violin on its carapace. (photo by L. M. Nakahara)

14

soon as possible. Ice packs around the wound may keep the poison localized. No fatalities have been reported from the Brown Violin Spider. No antivenin is available to counteract the venom.

Pale Leaf Spider

Cheiracanthium diversum (Fig. 9)

A yellowish beige spider of mild toxicity to humans, with most bites occurring on the fingers and causing intense pain and swelling that usually lasts a few hours.

How to Recognize:

This is a yellowish to yellow-green spider with fairly long legs. Both sexes have very large, long, pointed, reddish brown-tipped fangs. The female is about ⅓ to ½ inch long. The male is about ¼ to ⅓ inch long.

Where Found:

This spider arrived in Hawai'i from Australia in 1949. It is widespread in the Pacific and the United States and is found on all major islands in Hawai'i.

What It Does:

Pale Leaf Spiders are usually found on plants, where they spin tubular nests open at both ends. They may invade buildings and spin their silken tubes in corners of walls and ceilings. Both males and females are venomous.

If You Are Bitten:

Exposed parts of the body are com-

FIGURE 9. The greenish Pale Leaf Spider. Note the reddish-brown fangs. (photo by R. Heu)

monly bitten, usually a finger or hand. The Pale Leaf Spider often grips very tightly and has to be pulled free. *Cheiracanthium* venom is of medium intensity. There are many reports of bites by this species in Hawai'i. Most bites have been described as immediately very painful, followed by reddening and swelling of the bitten part, and causing mild to severe general reactions such as nausea, stomach cramps, dizziness, and headache. Recovery from pain and general reactions is usually within a couple of days. In some cases, skin may die and slough off at the site of the bite. If pain or swelling is severe, see a doctor promptly. Treatment is to alleviate symptoms, and antibiotics may be given.

"Daring Jumping Spider"
Phidippus audax (Figs. 10–11)

A black, furry, short-legged jumping spider that will bite.

How to Recognize:
Phidippus audax is small (males ¼ to ½ inches long and females ⁵⁄₁₆ to ⅝ inches long), short-legged, and furry. The abdomen is black with a white crossband and a few spots. The fangs are greenish.

Where Found:
The "Daring Jumping Spider" arrived in Hawai'i in 1937 and is known from O'ahu and Maui.

What It Does:
This spider does not make a stationary web but roams freely, hunting for small arthropods.

FIGURE 10. The "Daring Jumping Spider" showing the distinctive pattern of white marks on the back of the abdomen. (VWR)

FIGURE 11. The "Daring Jumping Spider" with its egg sac. (VWR)

If You Are Bitten:

Phidippus bites are sharp and painful and produce pale, raised bumps surrounded by redness, accompanied by blistering and swelling. The swelling can be severe, extending beyond the immediate bitten area, but usually subsides within forty-eight hours. A dull throbbing pain and itchiness may last several days. Treatment is usually not necessary other than with an over-the-counter pain remedy. If symptoms are severe or if complications develop, see a doctor.

Asian Spinybacked Spider
Gasteracantha mammosa (Figs. 12–15)

A spiny-backed spider that may make large community webs and occasionally bites humans. This spider is related to the Spinybacked Spider, *Gasteracantha*

FIGURE 12. The brownish, crablike adult of the Asian Spinybacked Spider. Compare this species with its relative shown in Fig. 15. (photos by J. Yates and VWR)

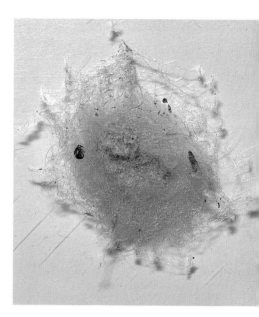

FIGURE 13. Typical community web of the Asian Spinybacked Spider, relatively high off the ground. (photo by J. Yates)

FIGURE 14. Egg case of the Asian Spinybacked Spider. (photo by J. Yates)

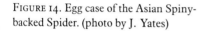

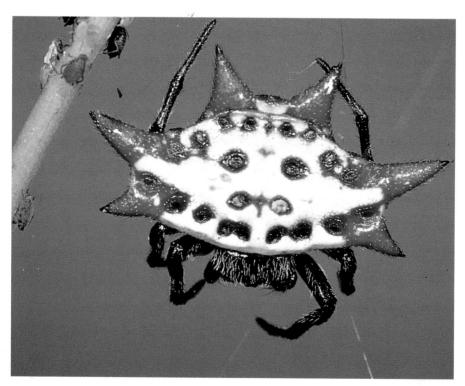

FIGURE 15. The Common Spinybacked Spider, typically found outdoors around houses. This species is related to the Asian Spinybacked Spider, but does not bite as readily. (VWR)

cancriformis, which spins individual webs in backyards, gardens, and forests. Their appearances are distinctive, and *G. cancriformis* does not usually bite.

How to Recognize:
Gasteracantha mammosa is medium-sized (about ½ inch wide), brownish, spiny, and crablike. The back has a series of spines around the edge and a couple of distinctive white spots in the center. The web is circular and has tufts of whitish silk attached to some of the radiating lines.

Where Found:
The Asian Spinybacked Spider was first discovered on Hawai'i Island in 1985 and since has spread to Maui, Moloka'i, O'ahu, and Kaua'i. This spider spins its web on trees, shrubs, telephone poles and lines, and other artificial structures, off the ground. It usually does not occur indoors.

What It Does:
Gasteracantha mammosa uses its web to trap insects. Occasionally people have been bitten when the spiders have dropped onto them or if the spiders have gotten into their clothing.

If You Are Bitten:
The bite is sharp and painful. Swelling occurs around the bite in most people. If the reaction is severe, seek medical help immediately.

Large Brown Spider
Heteropoda venatoria (Fig. 16)
Also known as Huntsman Spider, Banana Spider, Cane Spider

A large, tropical spider that hunts freely on the ground and occasionally enters

FIGURE 16. The female of the Large Brown, or Cane, Spider. Here she is shown carrying her egg sac in her mouthparts. She will not feed until the eggs have hatched. (photo by W. P. Mull)

homes. It looks threatening, but its appearance is much more fearsome than its bite.

How to Recognize:

This is a large, hairy-looking spider with a light brown body often over an inch long in females (smaller in males) and long, bristly, outspread legs spanning three inches or more. Large Brown Spiders are often mistaken for tarantulas, which do not occur in Hawai'i.

Where Found:

The Large Brown Spider is widespread in the tropics, and in Hawai'i is found on all major islands. These spiders usually live outdoors under tree bark and refuse, but are frequently found in houses and other buildings hunting on walls, especially in wetter parts of the Islands.

What It Does:

Large Brown Spiders hide in crevices during the day and come out at night, searching for food. They are generally beneficial, because they feed on cockroaches, flies, silverfish, and other household pests. Large Brown Spiders do not spin webs to capture prey or safeguard eggs. During egg-laying periods, a female may be seen carrying a large, white, pill-shaped egg sac in her mouthparts. She does not feed during this month-long period of protecting her eggs.

If You Are Bitten:

Despite its ferocious appearance, this spider rarely bites unless teased to do so, and if it bites, may not inject poison. However, it has been reported as biting and affecting humans in other parts of the world. The bite may feel like a slight pinprick. Reactions to the bite are pain, followed by redness and swelling, and possibly a raised bump at the bite site. If you are bitten, take normal precautions and see a doctor promptly if problems develop.

MITES
Subclass Acari
'uku hipa, ona, ona moa

Mites are tiny, eight-legged animals closely related to spiders. They are often only barely visible to the naked eye. Many are important in transmission of diseases. They may bite humans when they infest foodstuffs and furniture, can cause itching and skin inflammation, and may produce allergic reactions. The most important mites in Hawai'i affecting human health are discussed below.

Tropical Fowl Mite
Ornithonyssus bursa (Fig. 17)

Tropical Rat Mite
Ornithonyssus bacoti

Northern Fowl Mite
Ornithonyssus sylviarum

Straw Itch Mite
Pyemotes boylei (Fig. 18)

In Hawai'i, several species of mites are known to bite humans. The most commonly reported problems involve the fowl mites *Ornithonyssus bursa* and *O. sylviarum* and the rat mite *O. bacoti*. These occasionally bite humans when their populations are high or their usual hosts are unavailable.

How to Recognize:

These mites are very small, less than $1/16$

inch long, and light gray or yellow. They can be seen by the naked eye when moving about or when numerous.

Where Found:

These mites are found throughout the world. Fowl mites are usually associated with bird nests, and the rat mite is usually found on rats and in their nests. The Straw Itch Mite is usually a parasite of insects infesting grain or seeds; it occasionally invades homes, but in Hawai'i is more often found outside infesting seed pods of koa haole, kiawe, or monkeypod.

What It Does:

Fowl mites are usually parasites of birds. Most fowl-mite problems for humans in Hawai'i occur in the late spring or early summer as birds make their nests in and around homes. When fledglings leave the nest or birds die, fowl mites may invade homes looking for a host. These mites enter houses easily if nests are close to the house, in

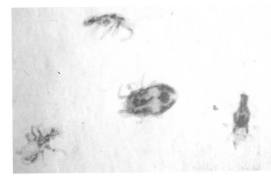

FIGURE 17. Bird mites trapped on tape. This is a good way to collect tiny mites and fleas for identification. (VWR)

FIGURE 18. Straw Itch Mite (round globules) engorged from feeding on a beetle grub. (photo by D. M. Tsuda)

gutters, or in attics, or if tree limbs touch the house and provide a route for hungry mites looking for a blood meal.

The rat mite frequently attacks humans when rats die as a result of trapping, poisoning, or destruction of their nests.

The Straw Itch Mite occasionally becomes a problem after treatment of homes for termites. These mites feed on the dead termites, build up large populations, and attack humans as the termite food begins to run out. Humans are also bitten by this mite when they handle infested seeds or seed pods or occasionally if the mites are blown onto them by the wind.

If You Are Bitten:

Mites inject saliva when they bite, causing irritation, intense itching, and occasionally inflammation of the skin. The bites appear as small white blisters surrounded by redness. Scratching may lead to infection of the bites. In some cases, there may be fever and other symptoms such as headache, nausea, vomiting, loss of appetite, and diarrhea. If symptoms are severe, see a doctor.

To prevent recurrence, the source of the pest mite (bird or rat nests, etc.) should be removed and the premises may have to be chemically treated. Destruction of rats or rat and bird nests may provoke additional attacks at first. If bites are severe, several members of the family are affected, or extensive areas of the house are involved, it is best to call in professional vector-control officers or exterminators to assist with removal of nests and with chemical control.

Mite bites are often difficult to diagnose and are sometimes mistaken for flea bites. Sometimes mites can be seen moving around on the skin. If so, it would be helpful to collect these into alcohol with a small brush or affix them to transparent tape (Fig. 17), taking care not to squash the mites. The specimens may aid in diagnosis of the problem.

Cheyletiellid Mites
Cheyletiella spp.

Cheyletiellid mites are parasites of dogs, cats, and rabbits and may become problems when humans have close contact with the infested pets, allowing them to sit in their laps or sleep in their beds, for example.

How to Recognize:

Like other mites dealt with here, these are tiny to microscopic. Diagnosis is often based on association with infested pets, correlation of symptoms with periods of contact with pets, and disappearance of symptoms after treatment of household animals. Mites are rarely found on humans when they visit doctors.

Where Found:

Cheyletiellid mites are found worldwide wherever their pet hosts are found.

What It Does:

Not much is known about the biology of these mites, but they apparently feed on blood or tissue fluids of their host animals. They may cause little or no symptoms on their pet hosts; or can produce slight to severe scruffiness and crusty areas composed of a mixture of scales, dried fluids, and mites; or may cause skin sores, weeping inflammation, and hair loss. Finding mites on pets may not be easy, but scraping lesions gently and examining crusts and skin debris under a microsope may turn up mites. When attacked, humans may have severe itching, skin eruptions, or blisters with a central pimple that tends to dry and slough off. Exposed arms and legs are most liable to attack, but lesions may become widespread on the body.

If You Are Bitten:

Application of calamine lotion or weak corticosteroid creams, in combination with antibacterial preparations, should be adequate. It is important that the source of the infestation be treated at the same time. All infested animals should be treated with anti-mite powders available from your pharmacy or veterinarian. Though it is not certain that mites can survive away from hosts, it is well to disinfest premises and pets' bedding to ensure elimination of the mites.

Human Itch Mite

Sarcoptes scabiei (Fig. 19)

A tiny, barely visible mite that causes scabies, or "seven-year itch."

How to Recognize:

This is an extremely small, oval, and whitish mite barely visible to the naked eye. The mite itself will not be seen, because it burrows under the skin, and its diagnosis must be based on the symptoms reported.

Where Found:

Associated with humans worldwide.

What It Does:

Human Itch Mite females tunnel under human skin to lay eggs and cause most of the itching. Males and larvae burrow less. The itch may be mild or excruciating and is usually, but not always, pre-

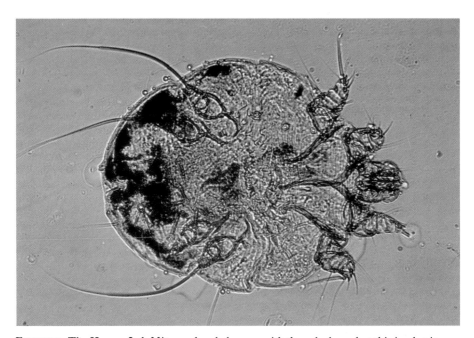

FIGURE 19. The Human Itch Mite can barely be seen with the naked eye, but this is what it looks like under a microscope. Notice the round body and tiny legs. (VWR)

dominant at night. It often starts after a person has gone to bed and becomes warm. Typically, in good light, burrows may be seen in the area of itching or skin eruptions; burrows look like fine, gray to white pencil lines, usually snaking around. A tiny, raised papule on the skin at the end of the burrow represents where the mite rests. After a period of exposure to the mites, hypersensitivity may occur, skin eruptions may become widespread, scratching may intensify, and secondary infection may set in.

A history of itching in other family members is an important characteristic in scabies. Often attacked are the fingers, between the fingers, the palms and feet, the penis and scrotum in men, and the areolae of breasts in women; lesions are not found on the face or scalp and rarely on the back or neck.

If You Are Attacked:

Scabies is easily spread from person to person. All family members and contacts of the family should be treated simultaneously. If an infestation develops, a doctor should be consulted for treatment. Ointments containing sulfur or gamma-benzene hexachloride have been successful in treating scabies. However, babies and young children, especially, should not be treated without consulting a physician.

House Dust Mites

Dermatophagoides farinae (Fig. 20)
Dermatophagoides pteronyssinus

These microscopic mites do not bite or sting humans, but they are included here because they affect the health of humans. They are widespread throughout the world, although they may be more important in Hawai'i and other tropical and semitropical areas. Two species are known: *Dermatophagoides farinae* and *D. pteronyssinus.*

How to Recognize:

These mites are tiny, invisible to the naked eye.

Where Found:

House Dust Mites live in the everpresent layer of minute dust particles that covers everything in houses, including floors, carpets, shelves, furniture, and beds. Species of the genus *Dermatophagoides* are often the most common mite found in vacuum cleaner sweepings, although other mites, including those that prey on House Dust Mites, are also found. The favored sites for mites are beds, which have the high humidity conditions these mites require and a ready source of food in the form of shed skin scales. When temperature and humidity are favorable, they will develop in other areas of the house, such as in carpets and overstuffed furniture.

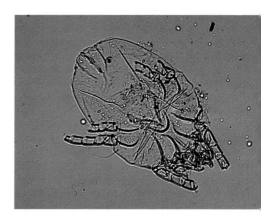

FIGURE 20. The tiny House Dust Mite lives in, and becomes part of, house dust. Many people are allergic to the mite or its parts. (VWR)

What It Does:

House dust mites produce asthmatic conditions in susceptible persons. Studies have shown that the mites themselves, parts of mites, their excretions, and their shed skins serve as antigens producing allergies in persons sensitive to house dust. Both mites and house dust can be brought to low levels by use of nonfibrous materials in bedding and frequent vacuuming. Tests are available to determine whether a person is sensitive to house dust, and, if so, additional preventive or control measures may be recommended.

TICKS
Subclass Acari
'uku hipa, nalo paka

Ticks are actually mites. Ticks are generally parasites of wild animals but also infest domestic mammals and birds.

They harm humans and animals by feeding on their blood, injecting toxins, and transmitting organisms causing diseases. Of the half dozen tick species in Hawai'i, only the Brown Dog Tick and the Spinose Ear Tick of cattle have been known to bite humans. Both rarely attack humans, and neither is known to transmit disease microorganisms in Hawai'i. The tick that transmits Lyme disease does not occur in Hawai'i.

Brown Dog Tick
Rhipicephalus sanguineus (Figs. 21–22)

A reddish-brown, common parasite of dogs.

How to Recognize:

Males and females before feeding are about $\frac{1}{8}$ inch long, flattened, and reddish brown. After a blood meal, the female may enlarge up to $\frac{7}{16}$ to $\frac{1}{2}$ inch in length and $\frac{1}{8}$ inch in width, and change in color to a grayish blue or

FIGURE 21. The Brown Dog Tick. The smaller male is on the left, the female before feeding in the center, and the engorged female after feeding on the right. (VWR)

25

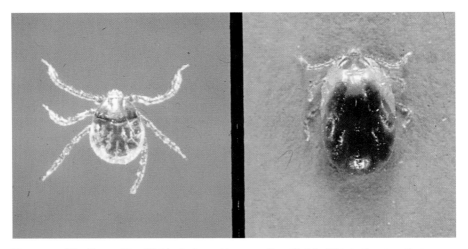

FIGURE 22. The Brown Dog Tick's six-legged larva, or "seed" tick. This is the stage that emerges from the egg. Thousands of these may be found in infested yards; they climb up on vegetation and wait for a host to come near. The larva on the left is shown before feeding, the one on the right after feeding. (VWR)

olive-green. Males do not expand as much after feeding. On a dog, relatively small males are often seen clustered around a huge, engorged female.

Where Found:

The Brown Dog Tick is found throughout warmer parts of the world and is probably the most widespread of all ticks. In Hawai'i, it has been reported from Kaua'i, O'ahu, Maui, and Hawai'i, but is likely to be on any island that has a dog population. In urban areas it is usually associated with dogs, but where dogs are scarce, other animals or humans may be bitten.

What It Does:

Ticks feed by inserting their mouthparts, or proboscis, into the skin of their host and sucking blood. The proboscis is armed with rows of backward-pointing barbs to help the tick stay in place during feeding, and this is why ticks are so difficult to remove once they have started feeding. After feeding and mating, adult females lay their eggs in cracks and crevices of the kennel or parts of the house frequented by the dog. Six to nine weeks later, the eggs hatch into six-legged, light brown "seed" ticks. The seed ticks eventually develop into nymphs, and the nymphs finally into adults. The seed ticks, nymphs, and adults all suck blood. This tick likes to crawl upward and if the infestation is heavy, may be seen on walls or ceilings, looking for places to hide.

If You Are Bitten:

A tick bite reaction is a slightly raised bump that quickly swells and develops a reddish halo. Some people react to the tick's saliva with intense itchiness. After the tick is detached, the bite may take two to three weeks to heal, leaving a hard lump that may last months, sometimes followed by a scar. The attached tick may be removed by grasping it as firmly and close to the skin as possible and pulling upward with steady, even pressure. Do not jerk or the mouthparts may remain imbedded in the skin and cause infection. Attempting to cause the tick to release its hold by burning its end with a match or cigarette will often result in a still-attached, dead tick. Antiseptic should be applied to the wound to help prevent infection. If the tick cannot be made to voluntarily release its hold, consult a doctor.

SCORPIONS
Subclass Scorpiones

mo'o niho 'awa, mo'o huelo 'awa, kopena, kopiana

Scorpions are eight-legged, flattened, lobsterlike relatives of insects and spiders. They have an additional pair of leglike appendages ending in pincers used to grasp prey, and also a long "tail" with a stinger at its tip. We have only one introduced species of scorpion in Hawai'i. Although there have been reports of other, larger scorpions, their establishment here has not been confirmed.

Lesser Brown Scorpion
Isometrus maculatus (Figs. 23–24)

A small, yellowish, brown-spotted scorpion that may sting humans in self-defense but whose venom is not dangerous.

How to Recognize:
This scorpion is light brown to straw-colored and usually about an inch or so long; some may be as long as 2¾ inches. When disturbed, a scorpion curls its tail with its stinger forward over its back, preparing to sting. Young scorpions are

FIGURE 23. The Lesser Brown Scorpion likes to hide under rocks and logs. Notice its excellent camouflage, which enables it to blend with its background and to surprise its prey. (photo by G. M. Nishida)

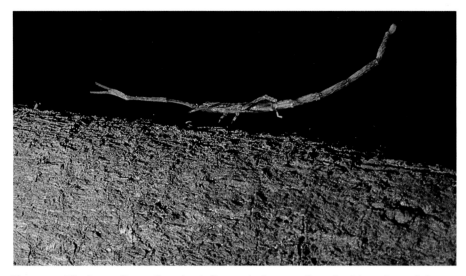

FIGURE 24. The Lesser Brown Scorpion is flattened when seen from the side, so it can fit into narrow places. The tail with the stinger is usually held down in this fashion and only moves up over its head when the scorpion is preparing to strike. (photo by G. M. Nishida)

carried about on the back of their mother after birth.

Where Found:

The Lesser Brown Scorpion is found all over the world in tropical areas. In Hawaiʻi it is reported from Oʻahu, Maui, and Hawaiʻi. It likes drier parts of the Islands and may be found in bureau drawers in the home, under woodpiles, in loose paper and leaf litter, under rocks and tree bark, and in other dark hiding places.

What It Does:

Scorpions feed at night, lying in wait for small insects, which they grab with their pincers and sting by a rapid thrust of the stinger over their head. The pincers are also used to hold the prey as the scorpion feeds. Scorpions also sting in self-defense, and humans may be stung when they reach under wood, into litter, or into other places where a scorpion is hiding.

If You Are Stung:

Hawaiian scorpions are not dangerous, but can deliver a sting nearly like the intensity of a bee sting. The sting may be painful for a few hours and some swelling and tingling may occur. Immediate application of an ice pack may reduce the pain. Recovery from the sting usually occurs within twenty-four hours. No deaths have been reported from stings of this species.

CHILOPODA

CENTIPEDES

kanapī

Centipedes differ from millipedes by having a single pair of legs on each body segment. Some people are unnerved by the wiggling motion of the centipede as it moves. At least twenty-five species of centipedes occur in Hawai'i, several of them native. Though several centipedes have been known to bite, only one introduced species regularly causes problems with humans.

Large Centipede

Scolopendra subspinipes (Fig. 25)

A flattened, wormlike, many-legged insect relative that may bite humans, causing intense pain and other localized, but not dangerous, reactions.

How to Recognize:

The reddish-brown adults reach six inches or more in length. The smaller, more colorful young usually have a greenish head with bluish antennae and legs. "Centipede" means "100-legged," but these adults actually have only twenty-two pairs of legs, one pair per body segment. They can move very quickly, propelling themselves forward with a wriggling, snakelike motion.

Where Found:

Known in Hawai'i since at least 1836, this conspicuous centipede is found on all major islands. It usually hides outdoors in dark places, such as under stones or boards, under bark of trees, or in cracks. Preferring moist situations, it may be driven from its hiding place by dryness, or occasionally by heavy rains. During these times, it may enter homes.

What It Does:

Scolopendra subspinipes is active at night and is generally beneficial because it feeds on cockroaches, slugs, and other such pests. Centipedes "bite" with the tips of the enlarged first pair of legs, which carry poison glands. Though they are longer than the rest and look menacing, the last pair of legs do not sting. Centipedes bite humans in self-defense, as when stepped on, grabbed, or squeezed while they are hiding in clothes or bedding.

If You Are Bitten:

Scolopendra's bite causes intense pain followed by swelling and reddening around the wound lasting a few hours. The wound is slow to heal and may become infected. The skin surrounding the wound may eventually die and slough off. Treatment other than antiseptic is generally not necessary, though an ice pack applied to the wound may ease the pain and help reduce the swelling. If symptoms persist, see a doctor.

FIGURE 25. The Large Centipede is shown curled around the young centipedes that have just hatched from eggs. Note the long legs at the tail end; these do not sting. The expanded first pair of legs behind the rounded head (near the center of the photo) house the poison glands. (photo by G. M. Nishida)

DIPLOPODA

MILLIPEDES
'aha

Millipedes differ from centipedes in having two pairs of short legs on each body segment, a tubular body, no poison fangs, and a vegetarian feeding behavior. Millipedes do not bite or sting, but can emit a spray or droplets of toxic fluid that may burn the skin and cause injury to the eyes of humans and animals. The fluid is used as a defense against predators.

No common name
Spirobolellus sp. (Fig. 26)

The actual name of this species is not clear and research is under way to determine the true identity of this millipede.

How to Recognize:
Spirobolellus ranges in color from cream to reddish with two light reddish or pinkish bands surrounding a thinner dark band running the length of the top of the tubular body. *Spirobolellus* may be up to 1¼ inches in length.

Where Found:
This millipede is probably an immigrant from elsewhere in the world. So far it is known only from Oʻahu. *Spirobolellus* is usually found under lumber, rocks, refuse, or wandering about, usually on the ground. It has been known

FIGURE 26. *Spirobolellus* sp. is a millipede that may cause chemical burns. Note the pale (to reddish) bands surrounding the dark stripe on top of the tubular body. (photo by G. M. Nishida)

to enter homes. It is active at night and may be found climbing walls.

What It Does:

Millipedes usually feed on organic materials and do not usually bother humans. However, this species has caused chemical burns on exposed parts of the body when induced to emit its defensive secretions. The effects of the chemical include staining and blistering. In homes, millipedes may stain carpets and flooring reddish purple with their secretions.

If You Are Sprayed:

Most people can pick up the millipede with their fingers and come away with just a stain. Other areas of the skin seem to be more sensitive to the spray; eyes are particularly vulnerable. Treatment consists of immediate washing of the affected area with large amounts of water to remove the chemical secretions. After washing, apply antiseptic. If symptoms are more acute, if they do not abate, or if the eyes are involved, see a physician.

COCKROACHES
Order Blattaria
'elelū, 'elelū papa

Cockroaches are included here because they are household nuisances, are known to carry disease microorganisms, and in rare instances may bite. Because they are usually nocturnal, cockroaches seen during the day often indicate an unacceptably high population. Bacteria and viruses may be picked up by roaches and transmitted to humans.

How to Recognize:
Cockroaches have long antennae, flattened oval bodies, and spiny legs. The forewings are partly hardened (though not as hard as those of beetles), and the hind wings are clear. All are very active, fast-running insects. Roaches also may have an unpleasant odor and emit nauseating fluids that contaminate food and the environment.

Where Found:
Cockroaches often invade homes and can become serious pests. They usually hide in cracks or other dark places during the day and are active at night.

What It Does:
In homes, cockroaches feed on a variety of items including bits of food, leather, hair, paper, starchy material, wallpaper, books, feces, blood, and even toenails. They will also feed on garbage and sewage. Cockroaches are known carriers of disease microorganisms; they pick up these microorganisms by feeding on, or walking over, contaminated material, and taint foodstuffs by walking, vomiting, or defecating on them.

Cockroach bites may occur where cockroaches are uncontrolled and have built up heavy populations. They may gnaw toenails and fingernails of a sleeping, sick, or helpless person, and bite into the surrounding flesh. Reports of bites are rare when good hygiene and cockroach control are practiced.

Some research shows that cockroaches may be as important as House Dust Mites in triggering allergic reactions to dust. See discussion under House Dust Mites.

If You Have an Infestation:
Good hygiene is important in keeping down infestations or preventing reinfestation. Removal of food sources and cleaning up droppings and stains will help make the area less desirable for roaches. Several commercially available baits and traps are effective in combating roach infestations. These are safer to use than sprays and powders, although they work somewhat slower. In severe cases, professional exterminators may have to be called.

American Cockroach
Periplaneta americana (Figs. 27–28)
'elelū kīkēkē
Also known as Water Bug, Palmetto Bug

The American Cockroach is large, about 1½ inches long, reddish brown, and its thorax is vaguely outlined in a cream color. Evidence of the presence of this roach are dark brown egg cases glued to surfaces (preferably wood), especially in corners; about sixteen eggs may be found in each case. In places where they have been feeding, large blackish-brown streaks of dried regurgitation occur.

FIGURE 27. The egg case of the American Cockroach is dark-colored and has a saw-toothed ridge along one edge. The egg case of the Australasian Cockroach is similar. (VWR)

Though its first reaction is to run, this roach flies readily.

Australasian Cockroach
Periplaneta australasiae (Fig. 29)
ʻelelū ʻulaʻula

The Australasian Cockroach is similar to the American Cockroach in size and appearance, but is slightly smaller and has a sharply defined whitish ring around the thorax and whitish slashes at the base of the wings. The Australasian Cockroach is more often found out-of-doors, but does occasionally invade houses. This roach also flies readily.

Brownbanded Cockroach
Supella longipalpa (Figs. 30–31)

The Brownbanded Cockroach is about ½ inch long and has two light brown crossbands on its back, beginning at the base of the wings and alternating with dark bands. The females have shorter

FIGURE 28. An American Cockroach female with egg case protruding at the rear. The thorax (behind the head) is outlined with an indistinct pale band. (VWR)

FIGURE 29. The Australasian Cockroach. A male (left) and female (right) showing the sharply outlined whitish band on the thorax and the pale bars on the wings. (VWR)

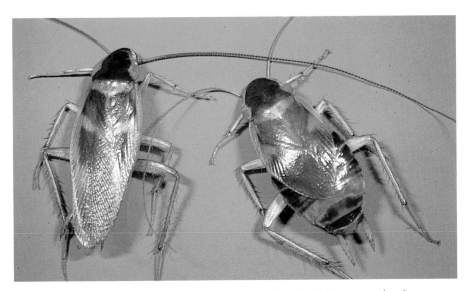

FIGURE 30. The Brownbanded Cockroach may be identified by the brown crossbands across its back. (VWR)

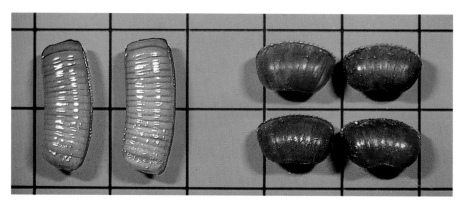

FIGURE 31. The egg cases of the Brownbanded Cockroach (right) are shorter and darker than those of the German Cockroach (left). (VWR)

wings that do not extend to the end of the body. This species is not as common as the German Cockroach and is often found in higher and drier locations, such as in picture frames, cupboards, television sets, and radios. The Brownbanded Cockroach likes to glue egg cases on walls and ceilings, especially in cracks and crevices and behind paintings and other objects on walls.

German Cockroach

Blattella germanica (Figs. 32–35)

This cockroach is about ½ inch long and has two longitudinal black bands on the thorax. The nymphs or young may have the bands extending down the abdomen. The German Cockroach prefers kitchens or bathrooms and loves warm places, such as under the refrigerator or next to the water heater. Though you may not see roaches, finding the light brown egg cases (Fig. 31) is evidence of their presence. The females are sometimes seen carrying these egg cases extending from their abdomens. Up to

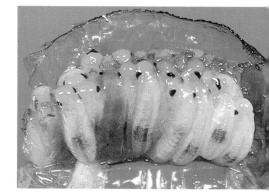

FIGURE 32. Eggs in an egg case of the German Cockroach, developing and hatching into nymphs. (VWR)

FIGURE 33. A male German Cockroach showing the black bands on the thorax. (VWR)

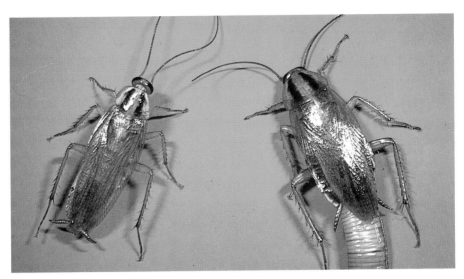

FIGURE 34. The German Cockroach has two parallel black bands that run lengthwise on the thorax. This is the species you will most likely find in your kitchen. (VWR)

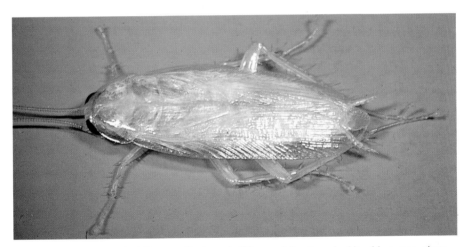

FIGURE 35. A newly molted German Cockroach. The roach has just shed its skin to grow into an adult. Within an hour, the newly molted roach will be normally colored (Fig. 32), and the wings will be fully expanded and hardened. You may occasionally see this newly molted form in your house and think you have found a white cockroach. (VWR)

forty-eight eggs may develop in each egg case. These roaches leave smaller streaks of regurgitation than the American Cockroach and also drop fecal pellets. The fecal pellets contain an aggregation pheromone, or scent, that attracts other German Cockroaches.

Burrowing Cockroach

Pycnoscelus indicus
ʻelelū lepo
Also known as Surinam Roach, Bicolored Roach

This roach was previously known as the Surinam Roach *(Pycnoscelus surinamensis)*. It was the first cockroach recorded from Hawaiʻi (1822). *P. indicus* damages underground parts of some plants, but it is usually a scavenger. Typically, this roach is found outdoors in loose soil or under objects on the ground. This species is often abundant on poultry farms and is an intermediate host of the poultry eye worm. The roach is eaten by the toad *Bufo marinus* and, at times, provides up to 50% of the toad's diet.

Madeira Cockroach

Rhyparobia maderae

This is the largest of the roaches found in Hawaiʻi, reaching about two inches in length. The species was first found in Hawaiʻi in 1896 or 1897. *R. maderae* apparently does not drop its egg case, and the young thus appear to be born alive. This roach has a very disagreeable odor and, if disturbed, may emit a squeaking sound produced by rubbing together parts of its thorax.

LICE
Order Anoplura
ʻuku, ʻuku liʻi, ona

Two types of lice exist, chewing lice (Mallophaga) and sucking lice (Anoplura). The lice discussed here belong to the Anoplura and are important to us because they are parasites of humans and other mammals. Lice have a long history with man and probably first came to the Hawaiian Islands with the Polynesians. The Hawaiian language has words and phrases that refer to lice, and some of the early Hawaiian literature describes how lice were eaten by the Hawaiians.

Head Louse

Pediculus humanus capitis (Figs. 36–38)
ʻuku poʻo

A tiny insect whose presence is not necessarily a sign of poor personal hygiene, but spreads by close personal contact.

How to Recognize:
Infestations are primarily recognized by the presence of eggs (nits). Lice are

FIGURE 36. Head lice nits (eggs) cemented to hair. (VWR)

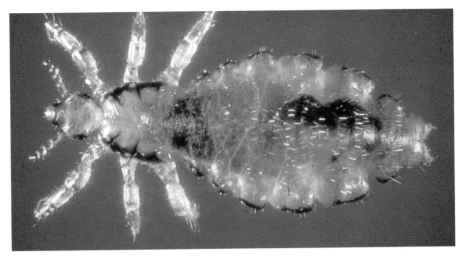

FIGURE 37. A closeup view of a Head Louse. These lice are known as *ʻuku* in Hawaiʻi and as cooties elsewhere. (VWR)

secretive and less easily seen in light infestations. Head lice are small ($\frac{1}{10}$ to $\frac{1}{6}$ inch long), grayish or creamy white, wingless insects. They are flat from top to bottom. The legs are stout and end in two claws. The yellowish nits are oval and about $\frac{1}{32}$ inch long.

Where Found:

Head lice are found all over the world in association with humans.

What It Does:

The head louse is normally found only on human heads, most frequently the nape of the neck and behind the ears. The adults use their claws to grasp hairs on the host and hold tightly. They feed by piercing the scalp with their mouthparts and sucking blood. Each female lays fifty to 100 nits. The nits are cemented to hairs near the scalp and remain visible even after they have hatched and the young lice have escaped. Lice are easily transferred

FIGURE 38. Closeup of Head Louse eggs cemented to hairs. After hatching, the young lice emerge through the top of the egg where the cap can be seen. (VWR)

between humans by direct contact or by infested clothing, combs, brushes, and bedding. Lice may occur even in sanitary conditions, particularly among school children. Crowding and unsanitary conditions encourage more severe infestations.

If You Are Bitten:

Head lice bites cause intense itching resulting in continuous scratching. Other effects of heavy infestations may be restlessness, irritability, and inattention. Extended scratching may cause infection, resulting in pain or tenderness in the affected areas, or even open bacterial sores. Severe infestations and heavy scratching may result in scabbing and discharge from the sores. Diagnosis should be made carefully, because dandruff or even fragments of hair spray may be confused with nits. If you have head lice, wash hairbrushes and combs, clothing, and bedding to prevent spread to other family members. Lice-killing lotions and over-the-counter medications are available, as are special combs to remove the nits. In case of severe infestations, consult a doctor.

Body Louse

Pediculus humanus humanus
(Figs. 39–40)
'uku kapa

Though not a major problem in Hawai'i, the Body Louse is included

FIGURE 39. Body lice feeding on a human. (VWR)

FIGURE 40. Body lice eggs in seams of clothing. (VWR)

40

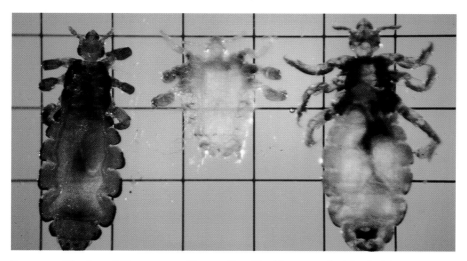

FIGURE 41. The three different types of human lice: Head Louse on the left, Crab Louse in the center, and Body Louse on the right. (VWR)

here as a potential disease transmitter. The Body Louse prefers areas of the body where clothing comes into contact with skin and is usually most abundant around the armpits, neckline, and shoulders. The eggs (nits) are laid on the coarse hairs of the body. The Body Louse is a carrier of typhus, relapsing fever, and trench fever.

Crab Louse
Pthirus pubis (Figs. 41–43)
'uku papa

A crablike creature most often found attached to pubic hairs; it feeds and defecates at the attachment site and causes intense itching.

How to Recognize:
Crab lice are tiny ($\frac{1}{32}$ to $\frac{1}{16}$ inch long), brownish-gray insects that are very distinctive in appearance. To the unaided eye, they may look like grayish specks. The broad, flattened, crablike body supports a narrow head and six

FIGURE 42. A Crab Louse clings to hairs using its claws. (VWR)

legs that each end in an extremely well-developed claw.

Where Found:
Crab lice are found worldwide in association with humans.

What It Does:
The powerful claws are used to grip hair and anchor the louse as it feeds. It usu-

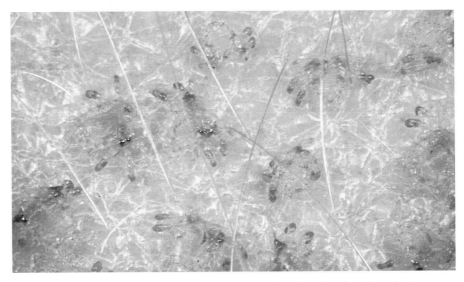

Figure 43. Crab lice showing droppings and skin irritation where they have been feeding. (VWR)

ally fixes itself to the coarser hairs of the body, such as in the pubic area, but may also be found on the upper legs, in the armpits, and on the eyelashes and eyebrows. After situating itself, the crab louse inserts its mouthparts into the skin, penetrates a capillary, and proceeds to feed. Lice are seldom seen moving. Nits (eggs) are affixed to the hair in a way similar to those of the head louse. Crab lice are spread by close physical contact, usually sexual intercourse, and sometimes by sharing of beds. Children under the age of puberty are not usually affected. Diagnosis should be made on the presence of nits or lice. The crab louse is not known to transmit any disease.

If You Are Bitten:
Crab louse bites cause itching, sometimes intense. The accompanying scratching may cause secondary infection. In severe cases, skin irritation may

occur and fever may result. If the infestation continues for very long, skin discoloration may occur. Lice-killing lotions and medications are available. In case of severe infestations, consult a doctor.

THRIPS
Order Thysanoptera
(Fig. 44)

Thrips are small ($\frac{1}{20}$ inch long), often dark-colored, slender, elongate insects that occasionally bite humans. Thrips are primarily plant feeders but some also prey on other arthropods. Most bites occur outdoors as thrips migrate or as they fly around vegetation. Their bite is surprisingly sharp, though usually no ill effects appear from the bite other than a small red spot or raised bump that may itch or burn. Swelling does not always occur, but the red spot may last

FIGURE 44. These thrips have been trapped on tape. The black, elongate insects occasionally bite humans. (VWR)

Bed Bug

Cimex lectularius (Figs. 45–47)
'uku lio

Bed Bugs emerge from their hiding places at night to feed on their sleeping human victims. Bed Bugs have been associated with humans for centuries and may have evolved along with prehistoric man. Despite much research, there is no evidence that Bed Bugs transmit disease organisms to humans. Its importance to humans is largely because of its bites and the social stigma

for several days or more. Some people may develop allergic responses to the bite or even to the insect landing on exposed skin. Responses in this case may be eruption of red spots or even inflammation in the nose and ears.

TRUE BUGS
Order Hemiptera
mū

Most bugs are plant feeders though some are predators of other insects and a few are parasites of vertebrates. Bug mouthparts are adapted for piercing tissue, so even bugs that are known plant feeders have the potential of biting humans. Those reported biting humans other than those listed below include water bugs, leafhoppers, stink bugs, and plant bugs. These bites normally do not produce any more than minor irritation or occasional redness at the site of the bite, though they may be initially painful. Several bugs in Hawai'i can produce a more serious bite.

FIGURE 45. A Bed Bug adult feeding on a human (its mouthparts have penetrated the skin). (VWR)

FIGURE 46. An immature Bed Bug, or nymph, feeding and filled with blood. (VWR)

43

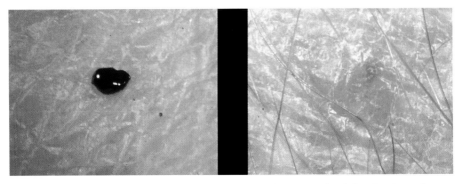

FIGURE 47. A Bed Bug dropping on the left, and a week-old bite on the right, showing redness and swelling of the skin. (VWR)

attached to having an infestation in one's home.

How to Recognize:

Bed Bugs are flattened, wingless, reddish-brown, oval insects, 1/8 to 1/4 inch long and about 1/8 inch wide. A short beak extends below the head. A Bed Bug infestation can be recognized by the distinctive odor emitted from the bugs' stink glands. Typical yellowish, redbrown droppings may also be seen on woodwork or walls. After feeding, the bug elongates and turns dark red.

Where Found:

Bed Bugs occur worldwide in association with humans. They are found in cracks and crevices, in furniture, beneath loose wallpaper, in the frames of beds, and in seams of mattresses.

What It Does:

Bed Bugs emerge from their hiding places at night or in dim light to feed on their human host. The bugs occur in clusters and are most frequently found in bedrooms, in hotels, and in other public gathering places where sleeping victims are available for feeding. They can be easily transferred on crowded public vehicles or easily introduced into the household in used mattresses and furniture, clothing, suitcases, and the like. Bed Bugs bite by inserting their beak, or proboscis, into the skin and probing until they pierce a blood vessel. Feeding is completed in three to ten minutes. Both sexes suck blood.

If You Are Bitten:

A Bed Bug bite is usually painless. Most bites occur on exposed surfaces such as neck, arms, and legs, and usually while the victim is sleeping. Bites are often multiple and arranged in rows or clusters. Sensitive persons may react to the Bed Bug bite with slight swelling or inflammation. A small round or oblong bump with a tiny puncture at the center is a common reaction. If you are bitten, apply antiseptic to the bite. In case of severe bites or reactions, see a doctor. Steps should be taken to eliminate bed bugs from the premises; they are easily controlled by professional exterminators. Cleanliness and care about introducing used bedding and furniture into the home are good preventive measures against the establishment of this pest.

Large Kissing Bug
Triatoma rubrofasciata (Figs. 48–49)
Kaua'i, O'ahu

Pacific Kissing Bug
Oncocephalus pacificus
Kaua'i, O'ahu, Maui, Hawai'i

No common name
Clerada apicicornis
Kaua'i, O'ahu, Hawai'i

Bites of these species may be quite painful, but not usually dangerous. Bites of the Large Kissing Bug may be followed by itching and burning, and the bite site may have a central raised bump. Application of antiseptic to the bite is usually all that is necessary.

FIGURE 48. The Large Kissing Bug can inflict a painful bite. It is recognized by the striped, flattened edges of the abdomen that stick out beyond the edge of the wings. (photo by D. M. Tsuda)

FIGURE 49. The Large Kissing Bug with its abdomen expanded after feeding. (photo by D. M. Tsuda)

BEETLES
Order Coleoptera
mū, puʻu, ʻūhini lele

Beetles are the largest group of insects. Beetles have the first pair of wings hardened and meeting in a single line down the middle of their backs. Some beetles can bite, but these bites are usually no more than a nuisance; they usually do not penetrate the skin. Beetles such as Blister Beetles produce a caustic chemical that causes burns and blistering. Blister Beetles (Family Meloidae) are not found in Hawaiʻi. However, other beetles that may produce similar effects do occur here. Rove Beetles (Family Staphylinidae) have been recorded as causing irritation and blistering. False Blister Beetles (Family Oedemeridae) have been known to cause dermatitis, and one such incident is noted below.

No common name
Thelyphassa apicata

Thelyphassa apicata is one of several species of False Blister Beetle in Hawaiʻi capable of causing skin disorders in humans. In one Oʻahu case, this beetle caused severe blistering on the buttocks of a baby after it became wedged between the baby's skin and diaper (G. A. Samuelson, personal communication). This beetle is slender and has long antennae. It is most common during warmer months and often enters homes at night, as it is attracted to light. It ordinarily does not cause any problems in humans.

FLIES AND MOSQUITOES
Order Diptera
nalo and *makika*

Flies are two-winged insects that include the mosquitoes and gnats. Mosquitoes are well known for their itching bites and for the transmission of diseases. Other flies may not be as well known, but they are often carriers of disease microorganisms. Hawaiʻi does not have some of the more notorious biting flies, such as the Black Fly, Sand Fly, and biting midges. Flies with biting mouthparts, such as the Stable Fly, pierce the skin to feed on blood. Flies with sponging mouthparts, like the House Fly, lap up partially liquified food. The House Fly apparently arrived in the Hawaiian Islands along with the Polynesians, as it was here before contact with Westerners. Although the Hawaiians popped lice and probably fleas into their mouths while grooming each other, flies were utterly detested and avoided if the insects were drowned in their food. Perhaps this indicates that the Hawaiians were aware of the disease-carrying ability of flies.

Mosquitoes are blood-sucking flies that are not only nuisances, but also may carry disease. Females bite and suck blood, while males feed on plant nectar. Mosquitoes were unknown in Hawaiʻi until about 1826, when the first species (*Culex quinquefasciatus*) was apparently brought here by a ship from Mexico; mosquito larvae were probably carried inside water casks. The Hawaiians were at first so intrigued by this blood-sucking insect that made its presence known by a "singing in the ears" that they gathered together during the evenings to enjoy the novel experience.

Eight species of mosquitoes are now found in Hawai'i. Five of these are harmful and three are beneficial. Hawai'i does not have the *Anopheles* mosquito, which carries the *Plasmodium* organism causing malaria. So even if humans with malaria live or pass through Hawai'i, malaria cannot be transferred to others because the mosquito vector is not here.

Mosquitoes inject saliva as they bite. The saliva acts as an anticoagulant so that blood will flow easily. The saliva causes swelling and itching that varies in intensity from person to person. Some people may develop some immunity and react hardly at all, but others may have swelling beyond the bitten area. Because scratching usually occurs, the bitten areas should be kept clean and antiseptic applied to scratches. Ice packs, antihistamines, and hydrocortisone creams may relieve the itching.

One of the best ways to keep down mosquito populations is to eliminate their breeding places. Most of our mosquitoes can breed in artificial containers like cans, bottles, old tires, and anything that collects water. By properly disposing of these eyesores, we can reduce mosquito populations. Another likely breeding place is the drip pans kept under plants, especially if they fill with standing water. Keep these containers dry or put a few drops of mineral oil onto the standing water (this is good for bromeliads). The oil prevents the mosquito larvae (wigglers) from penetrating the surface of the water to breathe.

Forest Day Mosquito
Aedes albopictus (Fig. 50)
Also known as Tiger Mosquito, Day-biting Mosquito

How to Recognize:
The smallish adult is marked with silvery white or yellowish-white bands and stripes on a black background. The legs are banded with white.

FIGURE 50. The Forest Day Mosquito has conspicuous black and white bands, is aggressive, and bites during the day. (photo by W. P. Mull)

Where Found:

The Forest Day Mosquito arrived in Hawaiʻi probably introduced from the Orient before 1896. It is commonly found in forests and valleys, as well as around residential areas of all the major Hawaiian Islands at both low and high elevations.

What It Does:

Aedes albopictus breeds in tree and rock holes and can also breed in artificial containers (cans, bottles, abandoned tires, plant-pot bottoms, etc.). Its flight range is a short 200 yards, so its breeding sites are likely to be nearby. This mosquito bites during the day. Its small size and hit-and-run biting tactics often cause people to wonder what bit them. This mosquito is a known vector of dengue fever. Fortunately, there has not been a dengue epidemic in Hawaiʻi since 1943.

Night-biting Mosquito

Aedes nocturnus

How to Recognize:

Aedes nocturnus is a medium-sized, brown mosquito with a band of white at the base of each abdominal segment; a V-shaped notch splits each white band.

Where Found:

This mosquito arrived in Hawaiʻi in 1962 and is found on all islands except Maui and Lānaʻi. Strong fliers, Night-biting Mosquitoes may travel up to twenty miles away from their breeding source.

What It Does:

The Night-biting Mosquito is not known to transmit disease but bites ferociously at dusk and after dark. It breeds primarily in flood waters and is occasionally found in intermittent pools and in pastureland.

Yellowfever Mosquito

Aedes aegypti (Fig. 51)

How to Recognize:

This mosquito is similar to the Forest Day Mosquito but has a lyre-shaped pattern (two parallel lines down the middle, surrounded by two outer curved lines) of silvery scales on the top of the thorax.

Where Found:

The Yellowfever mosquito arrived in Hawaiʻi around 1892; it is usually found on the warmer, drier sides of islands. The range of this mosquito in Hawaiʻi seems to be decreasing. Found previously on most major islands, *Aedes aegypti* now seems to be restricted to the Big Island and possibly Lānaʻi and Molokaʻi.

What It Does:

Aedes aegypti breeds in artificial containers as well as tree holes and other natu-

FIGURE 51. The Yellowfever Mosquito has lyre-shaped white markings on the thorax (behind the head); its range is now restricted to the Big Island and possibly Lānaʻi and Molokaʻi. (photo by Robert Trosper)

ral containers. It does not fly more than 100 to 150 yards from its breeding source. The Yellowfever Mosquito usually bites during the day, is often found near buildings, and prefers to bite humans. It is a potential carrier of yellow fever and dengue fever, and in the forests is a carrier of bird malaria.

Southern House Mosquito

Culex quinquefasciatus (Fig. 52)

How to Recognize:

The Southern House Mosquito is medium-sized, dull brownish or yellowish in background color, with uniform white bands at the bases of the abdominal segments.

Where Found:

This was the first mosquito to arrive in Hawai'i, probably in 1826. It is found on all islands and is the most common species in Hawai'i. This mosquito commonly breeds in standing water such as ground pools or swamps, but can also breed in artificial containers. It bites at night and ranges in elevation from sea level to 6,000 feet. It can fly up to three miles seeking a meal.

What It Does:

Culex quinquefasciatus can transmit encephalitis and filariasis. Its high-pitched hum and vicious bite make it the most annoying of the mosquitoes in Hawai'i. It is also the major carrier of dog heartworm in Hawai'i. Dogs in Hawai'i should be protected from these mosquitoes by bringing them indoors at night and by giving them preventive heartworm medication (prophylaxis).

Bromeliad Mosquito

Wyeomyia mitchelli (Fig. 53)

Wyeomyia mitchelli is a relatively recent arrival on O'ahu (1981); it breeds in water collected in bromeliad plants and will bite humans.

FIGURE 52. The Southern House Mosquito bites at night and is the major carrier of dog heartworm in Hawai'i. (VWR)

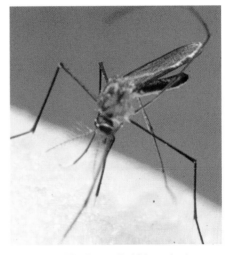

FIGURE 53. The Bromeliad Mosquito is one of the most recent mosquito arrivals in Hawai'i. (photo by L. M. Nakahara)

"Cannibal Mosquito"

Toxorhynchites amboinensis (Fig. 54)
Toxorhynchites brevipalpis
Toxorhynchites inornatus

The larvae of these three cannibal species of *Toxorhynchites* are beneficial, as they feed on the larvae of pest mosquito species. All three species were purposefully introduced into Hawai'i to control other mosquitoes. Adults of *Toxorhynchites* are large, have long, curved mouthparts incapable of biting, and are strikingly marked with metallic scales. These mosquitoes do not bite humans and should be distinguished from those that do.

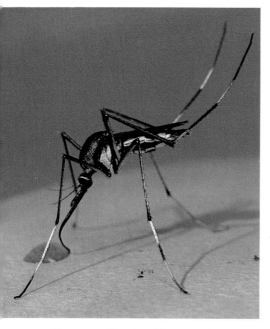

FIGURE 54. *Toxorhynchites* mosquitoes are large and fearsome looking, but they do not bite. Their young, or larvae, feed on other mosquitoes and flies. (photo by Frank Weibel and John Jaworski)

Stable Fly

Stomoxys calcitrans (Figs. 55–56)

A fly that resembles a light-colored house fly, but has mouthparts adapted for piercing the skin and sucking. The Stable Fly is more likely to bite when the humidity is high, particularly after a rain.

How to Recognize:

This fly is about ⅓ inch long, slightly larger than a House Fly, brownish gray with greenish-yellow sheen. The abdomen is somewhat checkered.

Where Found:

The Stable Fly is usually found around large groups of domestic animals such as herds of horses or cattle. They like perching on sun-drenched, light-colored surfaces. They may occur indoors in rainy weather. The larvae are usually found in soggy, decaying hay or grain, or other vegetable matter. The Stable Fly is found on all major islands in Hawai'i.

What It Does:

Usually a pest of livestock, it occasionally bites humans, usually outdoors. The Stable Fly bites by thrusting its mouthparts into the victim, usually during daylight hours. It often bites through clothing. Both males and females bite and suck blood. The Stable Fly is a possible carrier of bacteria and may carry cholera and tuberculosis bacilli.

If You Are Bitten:

The bite is quite painful and noticeable, so the bite victim usually chases the fly away. The fly is persistent and will continue to return to the bite to complete its feeding. A small swelling appears at the

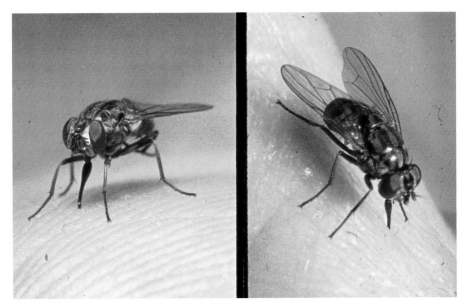

FIGURE 55. Stable Flies with mouthparts inserted, sucking blood. (VWR)

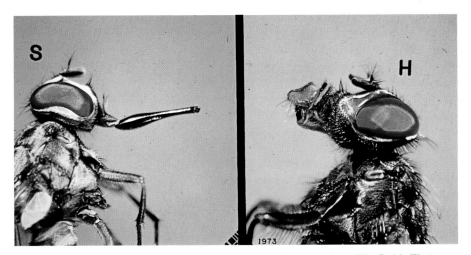

FIGURE 56. Stable Fly and House Fly mouthparts shown for comparison. The Stable Fly mouthparts (left) are adapted for piercing and sucking blood. The House Fly mouthparts (right) are spongelike and used for lapping up food. (VWR)

bite site and quickly dissipates. The bite seldom causes much trouble, unless secondary infection occurs. Application of antiseptic may help.

Horn Fly

Haematobia irritans

nalo ʻaki

The Horn Fly, ¹⁄₆ inch long, resembles the Stable Fly but is more slender. It is found on all major islands. The name comes from its habit of clustering around the horns of cattle. The fly larvae burrow into manure. Humans are rarely bitten.

House Fly

Musca domestica (Fig. 57)

Found on all major islands in Hawaiʻi, *Musca domestica* is closely associated with man. It feeds on anything with a moist surface, including food of all kinds, excrement, and garbage. These flies are important in breaking down organic debris, like garbage and manure. Diseases are spread when the fly picks up microorganisms by feeding or landing on contaminated material. It then contaminates food by walking over it, regurgitating on it, or dropping fecal matter. The House Fly can transmit viruses (e.g., poliomyelitis and Coxsackie), bacteria (e.g., dysentery, typhoid, tuberculosis, plague), protozoa (e.g., amoebic dysentery), and even tapeworms and other arthropod parasites.

Dog Dung Fly

Musca sorbens (Fig. 58)

The Dog Dung Fly is found on all major islands. *Musca sorbens* is important in Hawaiʻi because the larvae feed

FIGURE 57. A House Fly feeding on bread. The House Fly exudes saliva onto the food. This partially liquefies the food before it is sucked up by the fly. (VWR)

FIGURE 58. The Dog Dung Fly, female on the left, male on the right. This species looks like the House Fly but is smaller. (photo by R. Mau)

on, and break down, dung of all sorts. However, as adults, the flies feed on human food in addition to garbage and filth, thereby transmitting microorganisms. *M. sorbens* is a known transmitter of viruses, bacteria, and parasites. This fly is also attracted to open sores and wounds and may cause infection. *M. sorbens* is also attracted to eyes and may transmit certain eye diseases.

FLEAS
Order Siphonaptera
'uku, 'uku lele

Fleas are wingless, flattened parasites of warm-blooded animals. They are powerful jumpers. Fleas are known to transmit diseases, such as typhus and bubonic plague. The Oriental Rat Flea is usually the major carrier of these diseases, although the others may carry them also. Fleas probably arrived in Hawai'i with European or American ships sometime before 1809. The Hawaiian name for flea, *'uku lele*, means jumping louse or, perhaps more broadly, jumping bug. That name was adopted for the small four-string guitar that is so often identified with Hawai'i. The most accepted version of the origin of the name of the ukulele is that the rapid, jumping movements of the fingers in playing the instrument resemble the movements of fleas.

Cat Flea
Ctenocephalides felis (Figs. 59–62)

The Cat Flea is the species most commonly found around homes and is often reported biting humans; it is found on all major islands.

53

How to Recognize:

Reddish-brown, wingless, leathery bodied insects, flattened from side to side. The females are about $\frac{1}{16}$ inch long, expanding up to $\frac{1}{5}$ inch after a blood meal; the males are smaller.

Where Found:

These fleas are found worldwide. The Cat Flea is the most common flea in Hawai'i and is found on both dogs and cats.

What It Does:

Both males and females feed on mammalian hosts by piercing the skin with their mouthparts and sucking blood. Flea eggs are laid singly on hosts, drop to the floor, hatch, and develop into wormlike larvae that feed on dried blood particles, excrement, and other organic debris in cracks, crevices, carpets, or animal bedding. The black specks that might be seen around flea bites are not eggs, but fecal droppings. The larva eventually spins a silken cocoon and pupates. The adults usually develop in one to two weeks, but require some stimulus such as vibration, to escape from the cocoon. The adult flea can survive up to a year in the cocoon if there is no suitable stimulus. Humans are usually bitten when fleas are numerous or when the host pets have died or are no longer present. Some people are more attractive to fleas than others.

If You Are Bitten:

A typical flea bite is a small red spot surrounded by a reddish halo and some swelling. Two or three bites are often irregularly clumped in a small area because a flea may make repeated attempts to feed. Bites are most common on ankles, wrists, and legs, but may appear anywhere on the body; they seldom occur on the scalp or face. Some people react strongly to the bite and develop extreme itchiness. Other people may not realize that they have been bitten until later when the bite begins to itch. Scratching may cause secondary infection. The reaction to the bite usu-

FIGURE 59. Side views of the wingless Cat Flea. Note the powerful jumping hind legs. (VWR)

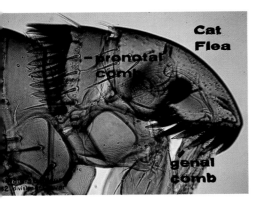

FIGURE 60. Closeup of the Cat Flea showing its "moustache," or genal comb, which helps the flea stay in place while the host is scratching. (VWR)

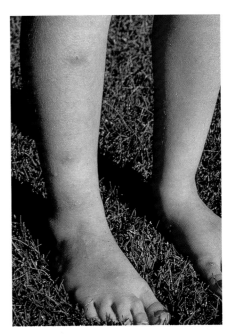

FIGURE 62. Flea bites on the legs of a child. (VWR)

Flea control in Hawai'i is difficult because the warm climate allows fleas to multiply year round. Flea eggs and larvae are continuing sources of pet infestation and also must be dealt with when attempting eradication. Flea bites may continue months after the host animal has died or left the premises. Once a flea infestation is established, treating the household pet alone will not control the problem. Treatment must include the yard and rooms in the house that the pet frequents. Treatment must also be repeated at intervals to ensure that all life stages of the flea have been killed. Professional exterminators may have to be called in difficult cases. The Vector Control Branch of the Hawaii State Department of Health can help with questions about control.

FIGURE 61. Top (dorsal) view of the Cat Flea showing how flattened it is from side to side, allowing the flea to move easily between hairs. (VWR)

ally disappears after two to three days. Sometimes scars are left in the bite area. Some people notice these scars, which turn purplish after taking a warm bath. If symptoms other than the localized bumps appear, see a doctor.

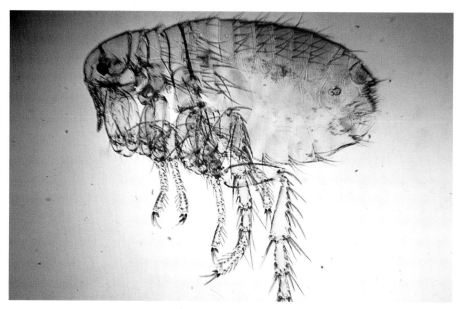

FIGURE 63. The "Human Flea," rarely reported in Hawai'i. Notice that it does not have the combs seen on the Cat Flea. (VWR)

"Human Flea"

Pulex irritans (Fig. 63)

The "Human Flea" is occasionally found in Hawai'i, but is rarely a problem; it has been reported from O'ahu, Maui, and Hawai'i.

Oriental Rat Flea

Xenopsylla cheopis

The Oriental Rat Flea is present on all major islands in Hawai'i. This flea, which parasitizes rats, may bite humans when there is an abundance of infested rats, or when rats have abandoned their nests. The Oriental Rat Flea is considered the principal vector of plague in the Old World. The disease has been present in Hawai'i since the middle 1800s, but there has been no outbreak of plague here since the late 1950s.

BEES

Order Hymenoptera

meli

Bees are extremely important because they are one of the major pollinators of flowering plants. The Honey Bee, in addition, provides humans with products such as honey and beeswax. Bees have stingers that are usually used to protect the hive.

Honey Bee

Apis mellifera (Figs. 64–65)
nalo meli
nalo meli pa'ahana   worker bee
nalo meli mō'ī wahine   queen bee
nalo meli noho hale   drone

A well-known, easily recognized friend of humans that stings only in self-defense. Most people suffer no long-term ill effects from Honey Bee stings, but the unfortunate few that are allergic to their stings may have their lives threatened.

How to Recognize:

Honey Bees live in well-organized colonies. Worker Honey Bees are brown and black with orangish rings on the abdomen and are about ⅜ to ⅝ inch long. Queen bees are slightly larger, up to ¾ inch long.

Where Found:

Honey Bees are cultivated by humans worldwide. The Honey Bee was introduced to Hawai'i in 1857 from California. The more aggressive Africanized Bees, or Killer Bees, are not found in Hawai'i.

What It Does:

Honey Bees pollinate plants while collecting nectar and pollen. The honey they produce is often harvested by humans. The bees are attracted to darker colors and rougher-textured clothing. The worker Honey Bee stings by thrusting its stinger into the skin of the victim. As the bee pulls away, the barbed stinger pulls out of its abdomen and remains in the skin. The poison sacs with the stinger continue to pulsate, injecting poison into the wound. The worker Honey Bee dies after losing its stinger. The Queen bees have smooth, curved stingers and can sting repeatedly. Drones or males have no stingers.

If You Are Stung:

Most bee stings cause a sharp, burning pain followed by swelling and itching around the sting site. Within two to three minutes, the red spot marking the stinger entry is surrounded by a whitish

FIGURE 64. A Honey Bee. Black and orange or yellow alternating bands are a warning to would-be predators to stay away. (VWR)

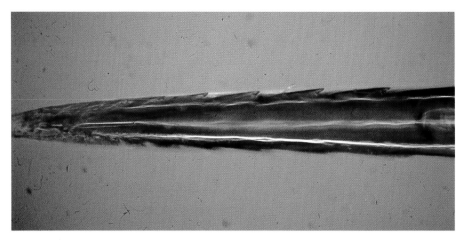

FIGURE 65. A Honey Bee stinger. The backward-pointing barbs keep the stinger in place while the muscles surrounding the poison sac continue to inject venom. (VWR)

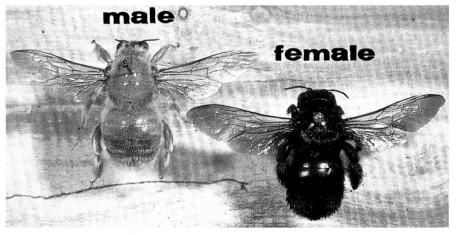

FIGURE 66. Carpenter Bees. These are very similar to the species found in Hawai'i. The females are black and can sting; the males are golden brown and do not sting. Carpenter Bees bore into wood to make their nests. (VWR)

raised area, circled by a reddish halo; the reaction normally lessens after a few minutes to a few hours. Some sting victims may have delayed reactions ten to fourteen days after the bee sting. Itching around the sting site may last for a few days. Greater swelling and rash lasting several days may signal a stronger reaction. A severe reaction may include nausea, diarrhea, headache, apprehension, difficulty in breathing, a drop in blood pressure, and dizziness. Serious reactions may include turning blue, loss of consciousness, collapse, or anaphylactic shock. If a serious reaction occurs, **get the victim to a doctor or**

hospital immediately. Those likely to have an allergic reaction should undergo a desensitization program or carry an emergency sting kit, with someone accompanying the allergic person instructed in its use. For most nonallergic reactions, merely removing the stinger is adequate treatment. The stinger should be removed by scraping outward rather than tweezing to avoid pressing more poison into the wound. Application of ice packs or use of calamine lotion, steroids, or antihistamines may help relieve symptoms. The sting site may become infected, so cleansing with soap and water and the use of antiseptic may help. Honey Bees are the cause of more deaths in the United States each year than snakes (but fewer than deaths by lightning).

Sonoran Carpenter Bee
Xylocopa sonorina (Fig. 66)

The Sonoran Carpenter Bee female is a large black bee that bores holes in wood.

Xylocopa sonorina is reported from all major islands in Hawai'i except for Kaua'i. It looks formidable, but it is shy and rarely stings humans. The male is golden brown and does not have a stinger.

WASPS
Order Hymenoptera
hope'ō, kopena

Wasps are narrow-waisted predators and parasites of other arthropods. Unlike the bees that have barbed stingers, the wasp stinger is smooth and can be used over and over again. Only female wasps sting.

Western Yellowjacket
Paravespula pensylvanica (Fig. 67)
hope'ō

A well-known and distinctive black-and-yellow-banded wasp that is aggressive and apt to sting without warning.

FIGURE 67. The Western Yellowjacket. Note how the wings fold into narrow strips over the back; they are expanded when the yellowjacket flies. The Western Yellowjacket is an efficient predator of other insects and is responsible for reducing populations of native insects in Hawai'i. (VWR)

How to Recognize:

The Western Yellowjacket is ½ to ⅝ inch long, banded black and yellow in color, with smoky colored wings.

Where Found:

Paravespula pensylvanica is an immigrant to Hawai'i, probably introduced from western North America. It was first found here in 1919 and occurs on Kaua'i, O'ahu, Maui, and Hawai'i.

What It Does:

Western Yellowjackets make large ground nests. The adults feed on nectar or similar fluids. They are attracted to bright colors and protein and may become pests at picnics or campsites. The adults capture other insects or spiders and pre-chew them to feed to their larvae in the nests. These wasps are aggressive and may sting without warning. They are especially aggressive if their nest is disturbed. The stimulus for defense of the nest may even be vibration caused by footsteps close to the nest. They also bite.

If You Are Stung:

The sting causes instant pain and a reddish swelling. After the pain eases, itchiness sets in. An ice pack at the site of the sting may reduce both pain and swelling. *Paravespula* wasps do not have barbed stingers like worker Honey Bees, so they can sting again and again. A sting may cause an anaphylactic reaction (see Honey Bee). If such a reaction occurs, **get the victim to a doctor or hospital immediately.** Also, because they live in colonies, more than one wasp may attack at once, possibly causing toxic poisoning. If stung by a large number of wasps, the victim should be taken to a hospital or physician immediately.

"Common Yellowjacket"

Paravespula vulgaris

Found on Maui. Habits and appearance are similar to those of *Paravespula pensylvanica,* but this yellowjacket is slightly larger.

Common Paper Wasp

Polistes exclamans (Fig. 68)

Found on O'ahu and Moloka'i. These wasps are usually not a problem except when they build their short-stalked papery nests in areas of high human traffic. They have a painful sting, but are not aggressive.

Muddauber

Sceliphron caementarium (Fig. 69)
nalo lawe lepo

Found on all major islands except for Lana'i. Muddaubers often build their mud-covered nests in areas of human habitation. They are not aggressive and rarely sting, but the sting may be painful and may cause hypersensitivity.

Other Bees and Wasps

Many bees and wasps other than the ones listed above occur in the Hawaiian Islands and are capable of delivering a sting. Most rarely do, unless mishandled. One should be careful around bees and wasps and if stung take precautions; if a severe reaction occurs, seek medical attention.

Figure 68. Common Paper Wasps chew bits of wood, making a type of paper that they use to create cells in which to lay their eggs. Paper wasps provision their nests with insects, often caterpillars. (VWR)

Figure 69. The Muddauber uses mud to make the cells that hold its eggs and young. It then stocks the cells with spiders to feed its young. (VWR)

ANTS
Order Hymenoptera
'ānonanona, lonalona, naonao, nonanona

Ants are social insects that live in colonies and work together cooperatively. Ants can be separated from bees and wasps by their elbowed antennae. Most ants are herbivores, but many are carnivores and predators of other insects. Some ants have well-developed stingers and inject venom into the victim; others may not have stingers, but bite and sometimes spray a chemical into the wound. The species listed here are known to affect humans. However, there are about fifty species of ants in Hawai'i; most produce complex chemicals that are used in signaling and defense, so it would not be surprising to be affected by one not listed here.

Fire Ant
Solenopsis geminata (Figs. 70–71)

A nonaggressive but potentially harmful ant.

How to Recognize:
The Fire Ant is light to dark reddish black with a large, smooth head. The petiole (the small, slender part between the thorax and abdomen) has a couple of sharply pointed bumps. Workers are ⅛ inch long and soldiers may range up to ⅓ inch long.

Where Found:
Solenopsis geminata is an immigrant to Hawai'i and is found on O'ahu, Hawai'i, Maui, and Moloka'i.

What It Does:
Fire Ants live in the soil in drier areas and feed on other arthropods and on honeydew (a sweet secretion) from other

FIGURE 70. A Fire Ant soldier with its large head (to left). Soldiers are usually found in the nest and protect it from intruders. (photo by L. M. Nakahara)

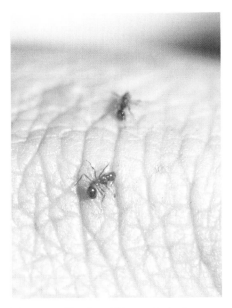

FIGURE 71. Fire Ants biting and stinging. The ant uses its mouthparts to anchor itself as it drives the stinger into the skin. (photo by G. M. Nishida)

insects. They prefer to nest in open areas.

If You Are Stung:

Fire Ants bite and sting. They grab the victim's skin with their mandibles while driving their stingers into the victim. Some people notice the bite and think it is painful, others do not. *Solenopsis* ants tend to sting several times without letting go with the mandibles, so the sting marks appear in characteristic small clusters. The sting is immediately painful, but the pain usually decreases after a few minutes followed by a burning itch. Usually within twenty-four hours, a raised area appears often followed by blistering that may eventually scar. *Solenopsis* ants may sensitize individuals after a first sting and cause allergic reactions from later stings. Hypersensitive

people may react with a severe itch ranging from tingling to pain. The pain may be accompanied by rash, faintness, blurring of vision, chest pain, and abdominal cramps. If stung extensively, there may be nausea, vomiting, dizziness, perspiration, and even shock. If a severe reaction occurs, **go to a doctor or hospital immediately.** Baking soda, calamine lotion, or hydrocortisone cream may provide some relief when applied to wounds.

Argentine Ant
Iridomyrmex humilis (Fig. 72)

Medium-sized (⅛ inch long), reddish-black ant with a sharply pointed node at the waist. This ant is reported from all the major islands in Hawai'i except Moloka'i. Reportedly a vicious "stinger," it has caused severe reactions. This ant, in fact, does not have a stinger. Instead, it bites and sprays the wound with a toxic chemical, giving a sharp burning sensation.

FIGURE 72. Argentine Ant. Note the sharply pointed node at its waist. (VWR)

No common name

Iridomyrmex glaber

Medium-sized (⅛ inch long), black ant. This ant is currently found only on Oʻahu. It is closely related to the Argentine Ant and is also known as a fierce "biter." *Iridomyrmex glaber* likes sweet things and invades households.

Mexican Ant

Pseudomyrmex gracilis mexicanus

Found on Oʻahu, usually in drier areas, *Pseudomyrmex* is a recent immigrant to Hawaiʻi. This ant is often found on kiawe trees or other plants that it protects from invaders, usually herbivores of all kinds (insects to cows). Humans are attacked if they shake or brush against the plant where the ants are stationed. The stings are painful, causing burning or throbbing around the sting site, with the development of large welts.

Pharoah Ant

Monomorium pharaonis (Figs. 73–74)

Several species of the genus *Monomorium* are reported from Hawaiʻi. In other parts of the world they have been reported to cause eyelid swelling and occasionally hives. If disturbed while biting, these ants may leave the whole head attached to the skin.

FIGURE 73. Pharoah Ants tending eggs and larvae. (VWR)

FIGURE 74. Pharoah Ants, showing the white grub, the worker, a black-winged male, and a winged queen. (VWR)

References _____

Alexander, J. O. 1984. *Arthropods and human skin.* Berlin: Springer-Verlag. 422 pp.

Biery, T. L. 1977. *Venomous Arthropod Handbook.* USAF School of Aerospace Medicine, Brooks Air Force Base, Texas. 49 pp.

Bonnet, D. D. 1948. Certain aspects of medical entomology in Hawaii. *Proc. Hawaii. Entomol. Soc.* 13(2): 225–233.

Bryan, E. H., Jr. 1940. *Insects we see in Hawaii.* Honolulu: Tongg Publishing Co. 128 pp.

Bryan, W. A. 1915. *Natural history of Hawaii.* Honolulu: Hawaiian Gazette Co., Ltd. 596 pp.

Ebeling, W. 1975. *Urban entomology.* Los Angeles: University of California Division of Agricultural Sciences. 695 pp.

Fullaway, D. T., and N. L. H. Krauss. 1945. *Common insects of Hawaii.* Honolulu: Tongg Publishing Co. 228 pp.

Gertsch, W. J. 1979. *American spiders.* New York: Van Nostrand Reinhold Co. 274 pp.

Gertsch, W. J., and F. Ennik. 1983. The spider genus *Loxosceles* in North America, Central America and the West Indies (Araneae, Loxoscelidae). *Bull. Amer. Mus. Nat. Hist.* 175: 264–360.

Haas, G. E., P. Q. Tomich, and N. Wilson. 1971. The flea in early Hawaii. *Hawaii. J. Hist.* 5: 59–74.

Hardy, D. E. 1960. *Insects of Hawaii.* Vol. 10, Diptera: Nematocera-Brachycera. Honolulu: University of Hawaii Press. 368 pp.

Hawaii State Department of Health. Undated. Mosquitoes. Vector Control Branch Bulletin No. 3. 2 pp.

———. Undated. Fleas. Vector Control Branch Bulletin No. 6. 2 pp.

———. Undated. Mites. Vector Control Branch Bulletin No. 7. 2 pp.

———. Undated. Brown Dog Tick. Vector Control Branch Bulletin No. 8. 2 pp.

———. Undated. Lice. Vector Control Branch Bulletin No. 9. 2 pp.

Hawaiian Entomological Society. 1990. *Common names of insects and related organisms.* Honolulu: Hawaiian Entomological Society. 87 pp.

Horsfall, W. R. 1955. *Mosquitoes: Their bionomics and relation to disease.* New York: The Ronald Press Co. 723 pp.

Illingworth, J. F. 1923. Early References to Hawaiian Entomology. *Bernice. P. Bishop Mus. Bull.* 2: 1–63.

Kaston, B. J. 1972. *How to know the spiders,* 2d ed. Dubuque, Ia.: Wm. C. Brown Publishers. 289 pp.

Levi, H. W., and L. R. Levi. 1968. *A guide to spiders and their kin.* New York: Golden Press. 160 pp.

Levy, C. K. 1983. *A field guide to dangerous animals of North America.* Brattleboro, Vt.: The Stephen Greene Press. 164 pp.

Marsden, D. A. 1979. Control of fleas. Hawaii Cooperative Extension Service Entomology Notes No. 9. 2 pp.

Mau, R. F. L. Undated. Farm and home insect pests—Scorpions. Hawaii Cooperative Extension Service Entomology Notes No. 12. 2 pp.

Milne, L., and M. Milne. 1980. *The Audubon Society field guide to North American insects and spiders.* New York: Alfred A. Knopf. 989 pp.

Papp, C. S., and L. A. Swan. 1983. *Ouch! A guide to biting and stinging insects and other arthropods.* Sacramento: Entomography Publ. 213 pp.

Pinter, L. 1983. Notes & Exhibitions. *Proc. Hawaii. Entomol. Soc.* 24(2–3): 184.

Roth, L. M., and E. R. Willis. 1957. The medical and veterinary importance of cockroaches. *Smithson. Misc. Coll.* 134(10): 1–147.

Schmidt, J. O. 1986. In *Venoms of the Hymenoptera,* edited by J. Piek, 509–537. London: Academic Press.

Service, M. W. 1986. *Blood-sucking insects: Vectors of disease.* London: Edward Arnold Ltd. 81 pp.

Smith, K. G. V., ed. 1973. *Insects and other arthropods of medical importance.* London: British Museum (Natural History). 561 pp.

Southcott, R. V. 1978. *Australian harmful arachnids and their allies.* Mitcham, S. Australia: R. V. Southcott. 36 pp.

Von Frisch, K. 1955. *Twelve little housemates.* Oxford: Pergamon Press. 155 pp.

Williams, F. X. 1931. *The insects and other invertebrates of Hawaiian sugar cane fields.* Honolulu: Hawaiian Sugar Planters' Association. 400 pp.

Wingo, C. W. 1978. Poisonous spiders and other venomous arthropods in Missouri. *Bull. Agric. Exp. Stn. Univ. Missouri-Columbia* 738: 11 pp.

Yates, J. R., A. H. Hara, and T. Y. Hara. 1990. Spiny-backed spider. Honolulu: Urban Pest Press, University of Hawaii. 2 pp.

Zimmerman, E. C. 1948. *Insects of Hawaii.* Vol. 2, Apterygota to Thysanoptera. Honolulu: University of Hawaii Press. 475 pp.

Acknowledgments

We thank the following persons and organizations for assistance and advice: from the Bishop Museum—Scott Miller, David Preston, Cynthia Fritzler, and Allan Samuelson; from the Hawaii State Department of Agriculture—Bernarr Kumashiro and Ron Heu; from the Poison Center—Lorin Yamamoto, Amy Shimamoto, and Robert Wiebe. Vince Roth, Jimmy Ikeda, Roy Furumizo, Gary Toyama, and Lawrence Pinter provided helpful suggestions. Ron Heu, Larry Nakahara, Julian Yates, Bill Mull, Ron Mau, Dick Tsuda, Robert Trosper, Lawrence Pinter, Frank Weibel, and John Jaworski helped with photographic materials.

Larry Allen, of Van Waters & Rogers (VWR), West Sacramento, California, supplied many of the color photographs; we greatly appreciate the help of Mr. Allen and Van Waters & Rogers in making available color slides from the company's vast library of pest-identification materials.

Index to Common and Scientific Names _____

Aedes aegypti, 48–49
Aedes albopictus, 47–48
Aedes nocturnus, 48
Africanized Bee, 57
American Cockroach. *See* Cockroach,
    American
Anopheles, 3, 47
Ant, 62–64
    Argentine, 63, 64
    Fire, 62–63
    Iridomyrmex, 64
    Mexican, 64
    Pharoah, 64
Apis mellifera, 56–59
Argentine Ant. *See* Ant, Argentine
Asian Spinybacked Spider. *See* Spider,
    Asian Spinybacked
Australasian Cockroach. *See* Cockroach,
    Australasian

Banana Spider. *See* Spider, Banana
Bed Bug. *See* Bug, Bed
Bee, 56–59, 60
    Honey, 56–59, 60
    Sonoran Carpenter, 58, 59
Beetle, 46
    Blister, 46
    False Blister, 46
    Rove, 46
    Thelyphassa, 46
Bicolored Roach. *See* Cockroach, Bicolored
Black Widow Spider. *See* Spider: Southern
    Black Widow and Western Black Widow
Blatella germanica, 36–38
Blister Beetle. *See* Beetle, Blister
Body Louse. *See* Louse, Body
Bromeliad Mosquito. *See* Mosquito,
    Bromeliad
Brownbanded Cockroach. *See* Cockroach,
    Brownbanded
Brown Dog Tick. *See* Tick, Brown Dog
Brown Recluse. *See* Spider, Brown Recluse

Brown Violin Spider. *See* Spider, Brown
    Violin
Brown Widow Spider. *See* Spider, Brown
    Widow
Bug, 43–45
    Bed, 43–44
    Clerada, 45
    Large Kissing, 45
    Pacific Kissing, 45
Burrowing Cockroach. *See* Cockroach,
    Burrowing

Cane Spider. *See* Spider, Cane
"Cannibal Mosquito." *See* Mosquito,
    "Cannibal"
Carpenter Bee. *See* Bee, Sonoran Carpenter
Cat Flea. *See* Flea, Cat
Centipede, Large, 29–30
Cheiracanthium diversum, 15–16
Cheyletiella spp., 22–23
Cheyletiellid mite. *See* Mite, Cheyletiellid
Cimex lectularius, 43–44
Clerada apicicornis, 45
Cockroach, 33–38
    American, 33–34, 38
    Australasian, 34, 35
    Bicolored, 38
    Brownbanded, 34–36
    Burrowing, 38
    German, 36–38
    Madeira, 38
    Surinam, 38
"Common Yellowjacket." *See* Wasp,
    "Common Yellowjacket"
Crab Louse. *See* Louse, Crab
Ctenocephalides felis, 53–55
Culex quinquefasciatus, 46, 49

"Daring Jumping Spider." *See* Spider,
    "Daring Jumping"
Day-biting Mosquito. *See* Mosquito,
    Day-biting

Dermatophagoides farinae, 24–25
Dermatophagoides pteronyssinus, 24–25
Dog Dung Fly. *See* Fly, Dog Dung

Fire Ant. *See* Ant, Fire
Flea, 53–56
    Cat, 53–55
    "Human," 56
    Oriental Rat, 53, 56
Fly, 46, 50–53
    Black, 46
    Dog Dung, 52–53
    Horn, 52
    House, 46, 50, 51, 52, 53
    Sand, 46
    Stable, 46, 50–52
Forest Day Mosquito. *See* Mosquito, Forest
    Day

Gasteracantha cancriformis, 17–19
Gasteracantha mammosa, 17–19
German Cockroach. *See* Cockroach,
    German
Gnat, 46

Haematobia irritans, 52
Head Louse. *See* Louse, Head
Heteropoda venatoria, 19–20
Honey Bee. *See* Bee, Honey
Horn Fly. *See* Fly, Horn
House Dust Mite. *See* Mite, House Dust
House Fly. *See* Fly, House
"Human Flea." *See* Flea, "Human"
Human Itch Mite. *See* Mite, Human Itch
Huntsman Spider. *See* Spider, Huntsman

Iridomyrmex glaber, 64
Iridomyrmex humilis, 63
Isometrus maculatus, 27–28

Killer Bee, 59
Kissing Bug. *See* Bug: Large Kissing and
    Pacific Kissing

Large Brown Spider. *See* Spider, Large
    Brown
Large Centipede. *See* Centipede, Large
Latrodectus geometricus, 12–13
Latrodectus hesperus, 9, 10, 13

Latrodectus mactans, 5, 9–12
Lesser Brown Scorpion. *See* Scorpion,
    Lesser Brown
Louse, 38–42
    Body, 40–41
    Crab, 41–42
    Head, 38–40, 41
Loxosceles reclusa, 14
Loxosceles rufescens, 13–15

Madeira Cockroach. *See* Cockroach,
    Madeira
Mexican Ant. *See* Ant, Mexican
Midge, 46
Millipede, 31
Mite, 20–27
    Cheyletiellid, 22–23
    House Dust, 24–25, 33
    Human Itch, 23–24
    Northern Fowl, 20–22
    Scabies, 23–24
    Straw Itch, 20–22
    Tropical Fowl, 20–22
    Tropical Rat, 20–22
Monomorium pharaonis, 64
Mosquito, 46–50
    Bromeliad, 49
    "Cannibal," 50
    Day-biting, 47
    Forest Day, 47–48
    Night-biting, 48
    Southern House, 49
    Tiger, 47
    Yellowfever, 48–49
Muddauber. *See* Wasp, Muddauber
Musca domestica, 52
Musca sorbens, 52–53

Night-biting Mosquito. *See* Mosquito,
    Night-biting
Northern Fowl Mite. *See* Mite, Northern
    Fowl

Oncocephalus pacificus, 45
Oriental Rat Flea. *See* Flea, Oriental Rat
Ornithonyssus bacoti, 20–22
Ornithonyssus bursa, 20–22
Ornithonyssus sylviarum, 20–22

Pale Leaf Spider. *See* Spider, Pale Leaf
Palmetto Bug, 33
Paper Wasp. *See* Wasp, Common Paper
Paravespula pensylvanica, 59–60
Paravespula vulgaris, 60
Pediculus humanus capitis, 38–40
Pediculus humanus humanus, 40–41
Periplaneta americana, 33–34
Periplaneta australasiae, 34
Pharoah Ant. *See* Ant, Pharoah
Phidippus audax, 16–17
Polistes exclamans, 60
Pseudomyrmex gracilis mexicanus, 64
Pthirus pubis, 41–42
Pulex irritans, 56
Pycnoscelus indicus, 38
Pycnoscelus surinamensis, 38
Pyemotes boylei, 20–22

Rat Flea. *See* Flea, Oriental Rat
Rhipicephalus sanguineus, 25–27
Rhyparobia maderae, 38

Sarcoptes scabiei, 23–24
Scabies Mite. *See* Mite, Scabies
Sceliphron caementarium, 60
Scolopendra subspinipes, 29–30
Scorpion, Lesser Brown, 27–28
Solenopsis geminata, 62–63
Sonoran Carpenter Bee. *See* Bee, Sonoran
  Carpenter
Southern House Mosquito. *See* Mosquito,
  Southern House
Spider, 9–20
    Asian Spinybacked, 17–19
    Banana, 19
    Brown Recluse, 13, 14
    Brown Violin, 13–15
    Brown Widow, 9, 10, 12–13
    Cane, 19
    "Daring Jumping," 16–17
    Huntsman, 19
    Large Brown, 19–20
    Pale Leaf, 15–16
    Southern Black Widow, 5, 9–12, 13

    Spinybacked, 17–19
    Western Black Widow, 13
Spinose Ear Tick. *See* Tick, Spinose Ear
Spirobollelus sp., 31–32
Stable Fly. *See* Fly, Stable
Stomoxys calcitrans, 50–52
Straw Itch Mite. *See* Mite, Straw Itch
Supella longipalpa, 34–36
Surinam Cockroach. *See* Cockroach,
  Surinam

Tarantula, 20
Thelyphassa apicata, 46
Thrips, 42–43
Tick, 25–27
    Brown Dog, 25–27
    Spinose Ear, 25
Tiger Mosquito. *See* Mosquito, Tiger
Toxorhynchites amboinensis, 50
Toxorhynchites brevipalpis, 50
Toxorhynchites inornatus, 50
Triatoma rubrofasciata, 45
Tropical Fowl Mite. *See* Mite, Tropical
  Fowl
Tropical Rat Mite. *See* Mite, Tropical Rat

Wasp, 59–61
    Common Paper, 60, 61
    "Common Yellowjacket," 60
    Muddauber, 60, 61
    Western Yellowjacket, 59–60
Water Bug, 33
Widow Spider. *See* Spider: Brown Widow,
  Southern Black Widow, and Western
  Black Widow
Wyeomyia mitchelli, 49

Xenopsylla cheopis, 56
Xylocopa sonorina, 59

Yellowfever Mosquito. *See* Mosquito,
  Yellowfever
Yellowjacket Wasp. *See* Wasp: "Common
  Yellowjacket" and Western Yellowjacket

About the Authors

Gordon Nishida has B.A. and M.A. degrees in biological sciences from the University of California at Berkeley and San Jose State University. Since 1975 he has been collections manager in the Department of Entomology, Bishop Museum, and has written numerous papers on insects and museum collections. He is in charge of more than 13.5 million specimens and his primary responsibility is to ensure that all these specimens are processed to scientific standards, protected from damage and deterioration, and made available for study to all who will use them properly.

JoAnn Tenorio is former director of Bishop Museum Press, former acarologist in the Department of Entomology, and, since 1989, has been the journals manager at University of Hawaii Press. She earned her Ph.D. from the University of Hawaii. Her academic training and interests lie with the medically important insects, mites, and spiders, about which she has written more than forty papers. During her seventeen years at the Bishop Museum, she responded to many phone queries from people interested in knowing what bit them.